WORLD SPACE PATROL
TECHNICAL OPERATIONS MANUAL

Chris Thompson
& Andrew Clements   Writers

Chris Thompson   Illustrations

Christina Logan   Additional Illustrations

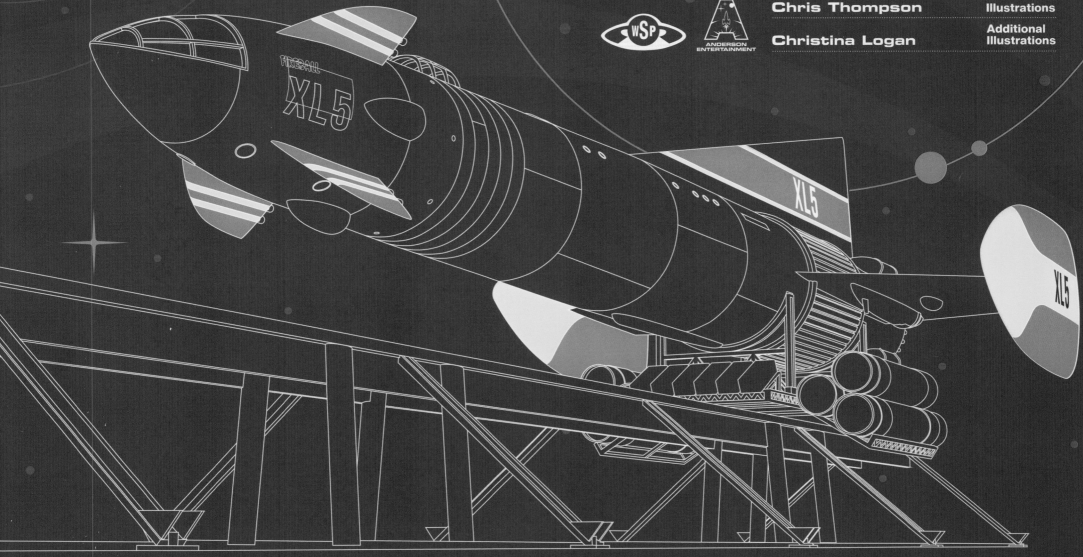

CONTENTS

THE BIRTH OF THE WSP

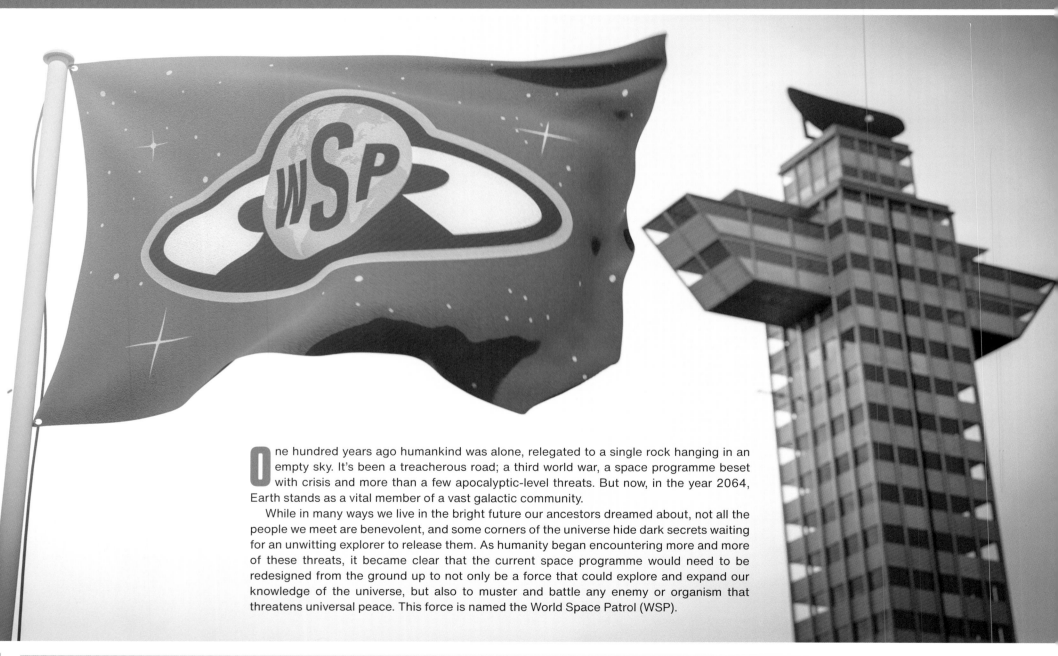

One hundred years ago humankind was alone, relegated to a single rock hanging in an empty sky. It's been a treacherous road; a third world war, a space programme beset with crisis and more than a few apocalyptic-level threats. But now, in the year 2064, Earth stands as a vital member of a vast galactic community.

While in many ways we live in the bright future our ancestors dreamed about, not all the people we meet are benevolent, and some corners of the universe hide dark secrets waiting for an unwitting explorer to release them. As humanity began encountering more and more of these threats, it became clear that the current space programme would need to be redesigned from the ground up to not only be a force that could explore and expand our knowledge of the universe, but also to muster and battle any enemy or organism that threatens universal peace. This force is named the World Space Patrol (WSP).

Following the establishment of a World Government in the wake of World War III, several space programmes – NASA, Eurosec and the SSP – were combined to form the World Space Agency (WSA). This merger allowed each part of the organisation to focus on various challenges that the new space programme would face, and encouraged the pooling of resources rather than the competition that had come before. By the 1990s, humanity had landed on Mars utilising a rocket made of components developed in China, Europe, Japan, Russia and the United States of America.

The development of the nutomic drive ushered in what is known as the First Expansion era. Spacecraft from Earth were now able to begin colonising the neighbouring solar systems and explorer ships began charting deeper into the universe. It was here that the age-old question, "Are we alone in the universe?", was answered when the TA3 came into contact with an alien trade ship. More encounters followed, mostly peaceful some disastrous, as a human vessel inadvertently invaded the territory of the nearby Astran Empire: the consequences of which still linger to this day.

Over the next few decades, humankind continued to grow in influence, expanding its borders and strengthening ties with peaceful neighbours. It became clear that the focus of the WSA should shift, not to focus solely on the exploration of space but on the security of what now constitutes its territory. For this purpose, the WSA was redeveloped and a new branch was established. Its mandate was simple: to facilitate the exploration of space, to protect humankind and its allies, and to offer the hand of friendship to anyone who may need it. The WSP's charter was officially ratified in 2046 and production soon began on a specialised fleet of spacecraft and a one-of-a-kind spaceport on an atoll off the coast of South America.

Despite the attempts of the interplanetary criminal organisation SOFRAM to undermine the formation of the WSP and steal the plans for the XL-class spacecraft that would serve as their vanguard, Space City officially began operating in 2050 and became the base where Fireballs XL-1 through XL-10 would blast off from to patrol known space.

At the time of writing, Space City has grown to be the biggest spaceport in the world and is the largest hub of interplanetary commerce on Earth. Its fleet of Fireball XL patrol craft oversee the 30 sectors of Earth's space.

The WSP has become a vital part of human endeavour in the 21st century. Not only is it the primary line of defence against the threats of outer space, but it has become an essential part of the intergalactic community providing security and aid to smaller alien civilisations that have either faced disaster or are unequipped to protect themselves.

As a potential recruit, this book is designed to give you an overview of the organisation, what we do and what would be expected of you should you enlist. To do this we will be focusing on the adventures of possibly the most famous crew in service today, the crew of Fireball XL5, as well as showcasing the command crew of Space City. Through the tales of their exploits maybe you will find you have "the right stuff" to be an astronaut in the WSP.

Section 1

SPACE CITY

INTRODUCTION

When the WSP's charter was first ratified, it was apparent that it would require a specialised base of operations from which to build, coordinate and launch its fleet of patrol vessels. As none of the existing spaceports were deemed suitable for this purpose, a large uninhabited atoll off the west coast of Chile was selected. At the time of its construction, it was the most ambitious and advanced project ever undertaken by a single government agency.

The location of Space City's island was remote and thus was clear of the usual space lanes, offered no preferential treatment to any one nation on Earth, and provided an additional layer of security with travel to the island being heavily screened. Until its official unveiling, the details of its design and purpose were classified as top secret. Although numerous attempts were made to uncover its blueprint by sinister organisations, these efforts were thwarted by the intervention of Universal Secret Service agents.

Space City has grown to serve various functions, such as becoming a hub for interplanetary commerce, a research centre and a venue for diplomatic talks, but its primary purpose is still to provide a base of operations for the WSP and its fleet of XL-class cruisers. While General Rossiter is the head of the WSP, Space City itself is under the direct control of Commander Jonathan Wilbur Zero.

While initially not that impressive to look at, much of Space City is either subterranean or scattered over different sections of the atoll.

THE KEY AREAS INCLUDE:

A **Primary launch area**
To the left is the scene people generally picture when they think of Space City as the primary launch area features the iconic control tower, the famous Fireball launch rail and landing pad 1. Beneath the surface lies a labyrinth of workshops and laboratories. Landing pads 2 and 3 are auxiliary areas that are designed to receive and dispatch spacecraft when landing pad 1 is full to capacity or is out of service. They are located a kilometre north of Space City and accessed by road.

B **Secondary launch area**
Space City continues to use traditional vertically-launched rockets as this remains the most efficient method of deploying large payloads into space. This type of vehicle carries a degree of risk, and as such the vertical launch area is located several kilometres from the tower with a protective bunker, Blockhouse Alpha, for ground crew to use during launch.

C **Airstrip and port**
Located on an atoll, the only access to Space City is by air or sea. The airport runway has been extended to accommodate interstellar liners while the port allows goods and supplies to be transferred directly from landing spacecraft to the mainland.

D **Beachfront**
While most of Space City's inhabitants live on the base itself, regulations have been relaxed allowing staff to start building their own houses on the north of the island.

E **Tracking station**
Located far away from the base and out of the way of incoming space traffic, the tracking station scans the skies above Space City for unidentified objects and potential threats.

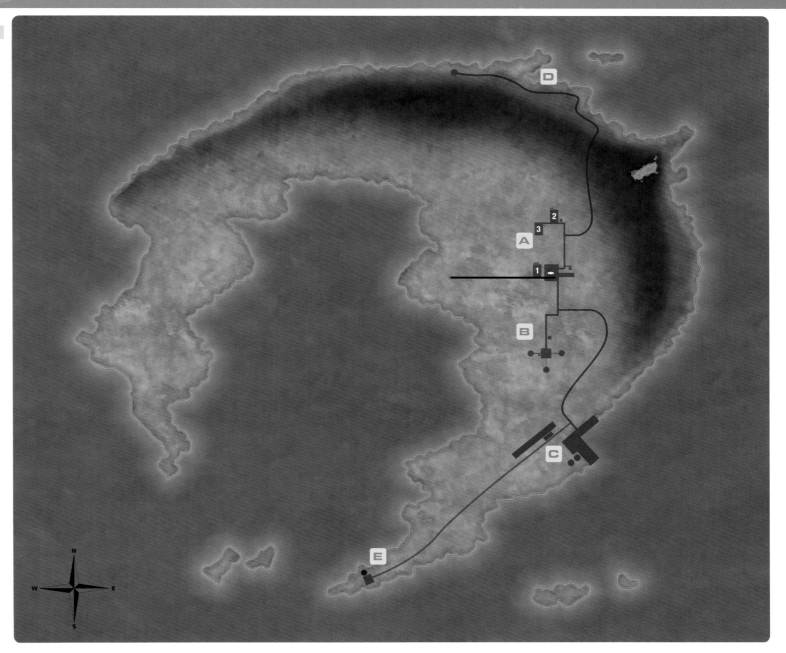

PRIMARY LAUNCH AREA LAYOUT

A Tower
Overlooking the primary launch area and slowly rotating to give a good view of both the secondary launch area and the auxiliary landing pads, stands the control tower. This landmark is visible for miles around and is the centre of activity on the base.

B Lift to Fireball hanger
Located parallel to the launch rail, a massive lift that transfers XL patrol ships to the surface forms part of the taxiway to the space rescue hanger. This is also where the lifting crane is stored. When not in use, a large cover folds into place to allow the taxiway to be used.

C Landing pad 1
Landing pad 1 is located on the reinforced concrete apron adjacent to the XL launch rail and the main surface complex. It is a multipurpose area that is most commonly used for smaller craft with a lift platform leading to the underground hangars.

The pad is served by twin cranes on rails positioned at the east and west ends of the apron: these cranes can be used to load and unload a wide variety of cargo and supplies. When unusual or hazardous cargo needs to be relocated, the mobile hydrocrane can be moved into position and used as a more precise alternative.

Two heavy duty fuel lines are used to resupply the craft using pad 1 and these, like all refuelling lines at Space City, are fed from the main subterranean fuel store to the east of the surface complex.

E **Emergency services**
Space City has its own emergency services including fire hovercraft, ambulances and helijets. These vehicles and their crews are based at the rapid response depot adjacent to the Space City launch rail. When an emergency red alert is called, the control tower sends a signal to the depot requesting the appropriate response. Many emergencies necessitate a specific response as standard procedure, for example, in the event of an emergency landing, the fire hovercraft are deployed to the appropriate landing area and take up positions with their foam cannons while ambulances stand by to move in if needed.

F **Space Rescue hangar**
The Space Rescue hangar is a surface-level installation which is large enough to accommodate a single Space Rescue vessel at any one time. The other craft remain on standby in hangar 1 below the surface.

The hangar is equipped with a separate refuelling system, a dedicated maintenance crew and emergency stores that can be loaded onto a craft at a moment's notice when precise details of an emergency situation are received.

There is also a short section of track that leads from the hangar towards the main launch rail which is long enough to allow the Space Rescue craft to clear the hangar before being lifted onto the launch rail by a pair of gantry cranes.

D **Launch rail**
Located a safe distance from the control tower, the several kilometres long launch rail is another iconic element of Space City. During launch, a hundred metre clearance zone is enforced around the launch rail while the initial boosters guide the Fireball craft away from the primary launch area.

Space City
CONTROL TOWER

By far the most striking feature of the Space City surface complex is the 25-storey rotating control tower. This impressive building is the central hub for Space City operations and all of the complex's most vital functions are controlled from here.

The decision to incorporate a rotation mechanism was taken during the early planning stages. In addition to offering the operations room a panoramic view of the multiple landing pads and launch rails, most of Space City's power comes from the atomic plant below the tower. The rotation of the tower itself acts as a gigantic friction generator, charging up emergency reserve batteries for use in the event that the reactor needs to be shut down.

The tower is encircled by a separate twin-storey residential ring at floors 4 and 5 accessed by a lift housed inside the cylindrical support strut nearest to the control tower's main entrance. The ring includes executive apartments for high-ranking officers and guest accommodation for visiting VIPs.

BASEMENT 3
The deepest level of the control tower houses the rotation gear mechanism, allowing the entire building to continuously revolve 360 degrees. The integrated generators convert the friction energy into electricity which is fed to the backup generator for use in the event of a failure in the main reactor.

BASEMENT 2
The atomic reactor is situated on the second basement level. Power for all of Space City is generated by the reactor and it is one of the most secure areas in the whole complex. Access to the reactor control room is by lift but in the event of a power failure there is a set of emergency stairs. In order to operate correctly, the reactor's air intake must be kept free of obstructions. The speed of the control tower's rotation can also be adjusted or halted from the reactor control room.

BASEMENT 1
The first basement level provides access to the tower's utility controls, freight lifts and independent backup power system.

FLOORS 1 AND 2
The two-storey reception hall provides a bright and modern welcome to the control tower while a nearby security checkpoint ensures that no unauthorised personnel are permitted access to the rest of the tower. All floors are accessible via a bank of lifts but only those personnel issued with special security electro-passes are permitted access above floor 15.

FLOORS 3–6
The main administrative hub of Space City is situated across floors 3 to 6 where all personnel from the finance and the human resources departments carry out their daily duties.

FLOORS 7–10
Space City maintains a fully staffed hospital wing across four levels from floors 7 to 10. The entrance reception is located on floor 7 from where the other three hospital floors can be accessed. In addition to the main tower lifts, the hospital wing is accessible via a dedicated stretcher lift. As with a standalone hospital, Space City's hospital wing includes a host of recovery rooms, private rooms, an isolation room, medical offices, surgeries, labs, equipment stores and two state-of-the-art operating theatres.

FLOORS 11–14
Four levels of offices and expansion space are situated between the hospital wing and the staff canteen. Many of these offices are used by representatives of the United Planets Organisation and the Neutral Planets Scientific Organisation, as well as liaisons to department S21 at the Pentagon. Weekly morale-boosting bingo nights are held in room 1401.

FLOOR 15
The staff canteen is located on floor 15 and has remained a firm favourite with the personnel in the control tower since it first opened. Patrons can select from a varied and constantly changing menu, and there is always something available for everyone's taste.

Floor 15 is also the highest level that anyone without top-level security clearance is permitted to access.

FLOOR 16
A viewing theatre is located on floor 16 used to view mission tapes once they have been processed in one of the adjacent film laboratories.

FLOOR 17
Floor 17 is dedicated to meeting rooms and top secret planning offices.

FLOOR 18
The classified control tower administration office is found on floor 18. This section works independently of those lower in the tower, and deals exclusively with the administrative needs of personnel and projects with the highest security clearance.

FLOOR 19
The computer room is situated on floor 19 and plays a vital role in each of the many complex calculations performed every day at Space City. Banks of computers line the walls of this space-age electronic wonderland: each computer bank is so compact it only requires four personnel to move it.

FLOOR 20
The communications centre is situated on floor 20 directly below the primary control room. Every piece of information received or transmitted from Space City passes through this room which is packed with sophisticated filters, decoders and signalling equipment of every kind imaginable.

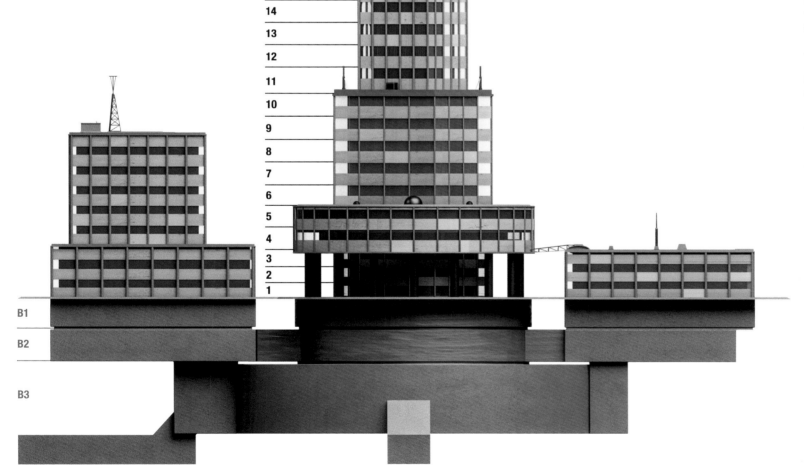

NEUTRONI ANTENNA

The neutroni antenna is the single most vital piece of equipment in Space City's communication network. It is capable of broadcasting and receiving signals almost instantaneously across vast distances of space.

FLOORS 21–22

Floors 21 and 22 form a two-storey split-level that is segregated into three separate sections. The central section within the tower itself houses the main control room where every major process in Space City is monitored and controlled including refuelling schedules, craft movements, crew rotations and emergency procedures.

To one side of the control room in one of the two 'flying bridges' that extend from floors 21 and 22, is the operations room. This room is manned by Commander Zero and Lieutenant Ninety and is perhaps the most vital room in all of Space City. It is from here that all executive command decisions are made and it is where Space City is actively run from.

The 'flying bridge' on the opposite side of the tower is home to the officers' restaurant on floor 21, with a separate bar area on floor 22.

FLOORS 23–24

Services including the primary air conditioning plant and the elevator maintenance area are accessible on floors 23 and 24.

FLOOR 25

Floor 25 is dedicated to signal processing equipment and the rotation gear mechanism for the neutroni antenna one level above on the roof of the control tower. The neutroni antenna can be rotated independently of the tower's rotation.

OPERATIONS ROOM

The operations room is the operational nerve centre of Space City which acts as the crux of a vast information network spanning the entire organisation.

The operations room contains some of the most advanced equipment ever developed including the space radar system, neutroni transmitter unit upgraded with a D400 Mk.X receiver in 2063, radioscope apparatus, space echo comm system, status chart for approach, landing and standby craft, and the early warning system.

A Commander's desk
From here, Commander Zero runs the WSP. His desk is fitted with its own independent neutroni transmitter unit that he can use to contact active spacecraft on his personal clear frequency.

B Controller's desk
While the commander is in charge of running the organisation, the controller is responsible for the operational running of Space City. From here, Lieutenant Ninety coordinates incoming and outgoing traffic landing at the spaceport.

C Upper viewing deck
For visiting dignitaries that may want to observe the running of Space City as well as access to maintain the upper windows.

D Space radar
A radar system that is fed information from various radio telescopes from around Earth. This helps coordinate spacecraft while also identifying potential threats.

E Operations screen
One of two monitors on either side of the room used to display a variety of mission critical information.

F Star map
A detailed set of star maps on Sectors 1 through 30, the maps are loaded on a cylindrical drum that can be rotated to show the relevant area.

G Access to lift shaft

H Access to the communications room and upper level

COMMUNICATIONS

The large empty space in the middle of the room is designed to allow more equipment and components to be added during specific missions, for example, when Professor Matic installed a long distance communications array or when film crews needed the space to film the visit of General Rossiter.

XL HANGARS

The underground complex below Space City is dominated by a huge network of bays dedicated to the Fireball fleet. Ten bays allow an XL craft to be stored, maintained and quickly cycled out to the rail when it is time to launch.

Given the size of these craft, a special rail network needs to be used to manoeuvre them to the correct part of the hangar or onto the lift to the surface. This requires careful planning and precise timetabling in order to make sure that only one patrol ship is using the rail at any given time.

Despite their massive size, space inside these hangar bays is tight and careful scheduling is required to make sure everything is where it needs to be and that there is always a clear bay for returning patrol ships.

Space Rescue 2 is housed in its own hangar close to the surface lift. If SR1 is launched, then SR2 will be moved to the surface hangar ready for quick deployment in an emergency.

Should, for whatever reason, all 30 Fireball's need to be grounded, further hangar space is located beside landing pad 2. This would be unlikely, however, as the rolling patrol schedule means that a maximum of nine Fireballs are housed in the main hangar at any one time.

SURFACE STORAGE

Craft are often kept on the surface overnight pending pre-flight checks. As per standard procedure, the next Fireball requisitioned to launch will be taken to the rail as soon as it is available in order to ensure that at least one vessel is always ready for immediate deployment. If a Fireball needs to be turned around in a hurry then it may vertically land on the launch sled on the rail for a quick resupply and relaunch.

LIFTING CRANE

In order to make the transfer of the patrol ship to the launch rail quick and efficient, the crane that will carry the craft the final leg onto the rail is attached to the lift from the hangar. As the vessel is raised by the lift, ground crews can attach the lifting cables and have the craft already aloft by the time the lift reaches the surface.

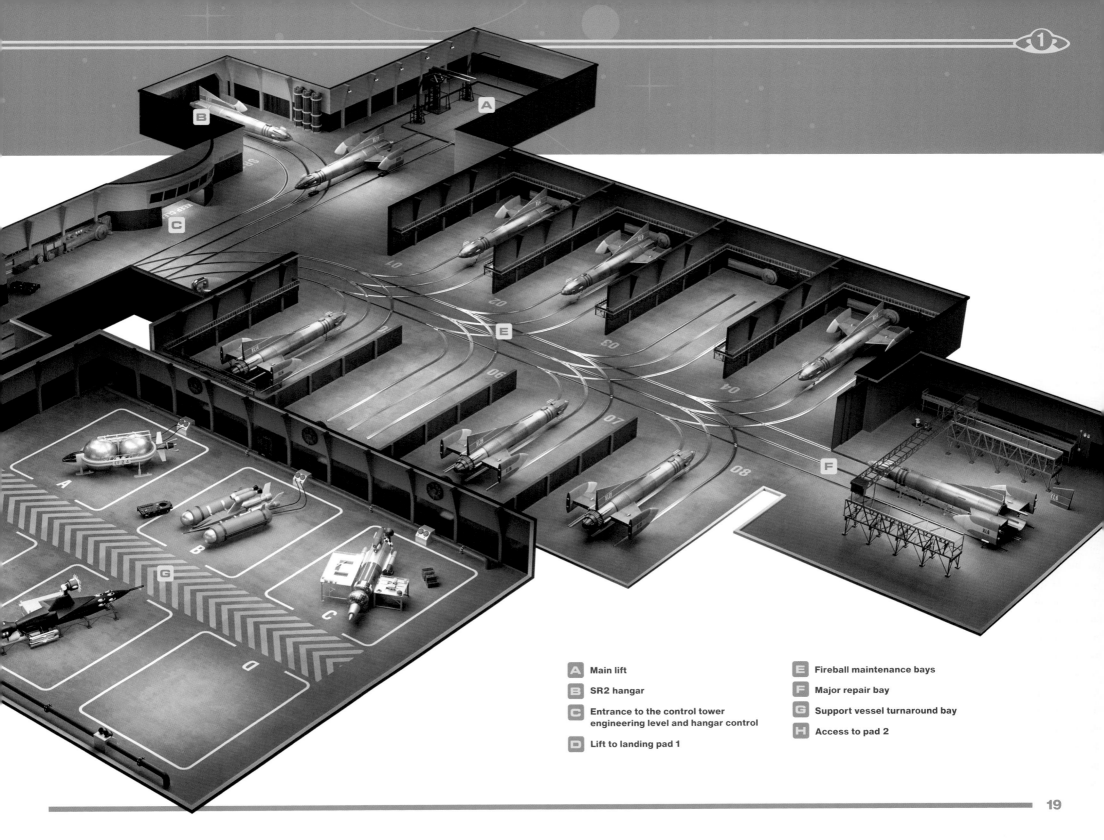

1

A Main lift

B SR2 hangar

C Entrance to the control tower engineering level and hangar control

D Lift to landing pad 1

E Fireball maintenance bays

F Major repair bay

G Support vessel turnaround bay

H Access to pad 2

XL PROJECTS WORKSHOP

Professor Matic maintains a personal XL projects workshop located, for safety reasons, a short jetmobile ride away from the primary launch area among a cluster of other science laboratories deemed too dangerous to be housed on-site.

A	Pedestrian entrance	**D**	Assembly area
B	Vehicular entrance	**E**	Tool shelf
C	Work bench	**F**	Sensitive equipment store
		G	Entrance to simulator room

The Professor is incredibly discerning when it comes to admitting entry to the workshop, particularly if he is actively working on a new project. Among some of the notable pieces of technology housed in the workshop are the Fireball XL5 simulator room and the Professor's time machine which is currently being assessed by the Saturn-based Interplanetary Patents Commission.

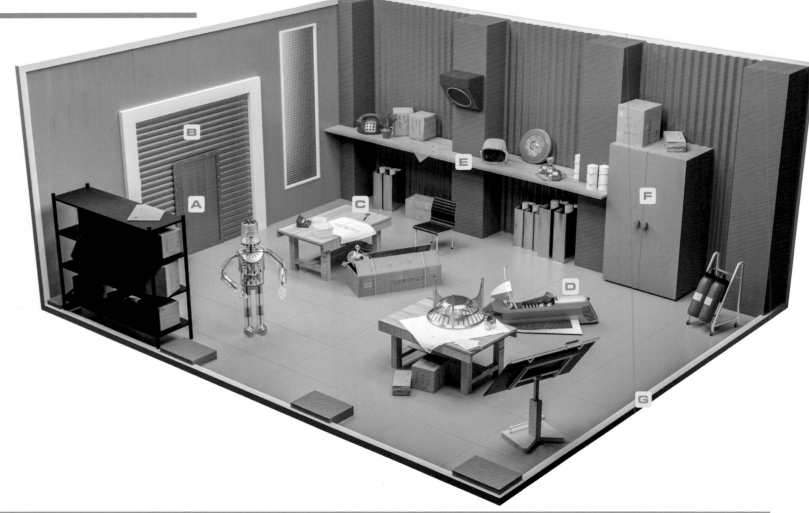

DECONTAMINATION UNIT

Space City's decontamination unit is located adjacent to landing pad 1.

When a contaminated vessel is granted landing clearance, two decontamination ray generators move along the rails on either side of the pad sterilising the outer hull of the craft. Next, a hydrocrane lowers a decontamination cell into the vessel and the crew enters the cell and seals the hatch. The cell is then winched out of the vessel and deposited into the decontamination building where the crew's vital signs and contaminant levels can be closely monitored on a set of highly sensitive equipment.

A	Containment cell	D	Control console
B	Decontamination rays	E	Protective screen
C	Exit to airlock	F	Intercom system
		G	Exit

CONTAMINATED VESSEL DRILL

Space City has a comprehensive drill for receiving potentially hazardous contaminated vessels but they still require notice in order to put their procedures into action. A quarantined vessel will most often be put into a holding orbit while the ray generators are moved into position and the pad is cleared.

SPACE CITY SERVICES

Just west of the control tower is the Space City services building known as Block Bravo. This nine-storey building is home to a wide variety of essential services, not least of which is the vital engineering and maintenance department.

The Space City Patrol (SCP) have their headquarters here, including the holding cells of Space City's famously impregnable jail. The SCP not only enforce the law, help to keep the peace and ensure the population stay safe, but they are also a vital part of Space City's perimeter security response. A network of guard towers and searchlights help to deter intruders from gaining access to the secure areas of the complex.

Space City's armoury is located on the south side of the services building and requires the use of an authorised security electro-pass before entry can be permitted. The armoury contains stun rifles, coma rays and other small arms.

Space City's own research and development department is based on the eighth floor of the building, although the majority of research for the WSP is carried out off-site in various installations across the United States of America and further afield.

The antenna atop the building is utilised by several broadcasters inside Block Bravo. These include Interplanetary News (who also provide the free daily newspaper to all Space City residents), Earth Television and the popular entertainment show *Space City Television Network Presents to the Galaxy* which is hosted by Johnny Jackson.

RECREATIONAL AREAS

While primarily a scientific and military instillation, Space City features many amenities in order to make life for the permanent staff on base more comfortable.

STANDARD QUARTERS

Located in the ring around the control tower, Space City's residential block offers a number of both single and shared quarters for key personnel and guests stationed at the base.

Each apartment is luxurious compared with similar accommodation in other government services. In addition to standard amenities, they feature the very latest in relaxation and entertainment facilities.

The living quarters for junior officers and their families are located in a dedicated residential apartment block several kilometres from Space City, with a regular hoverbus service providing access from the apartments to the main complex.

ARCADE AND LEISURE COMPLEX

The arcade and leisure facilities are located in the smallest of the three structures adjacent to the launch rail. Sometimes referred to as Block Charlie, the surface building is the entrance to a much larger subterranean arcade which contains almost everything the population of Space City would otherwise be able to find in a big city. The sprawling mall is filled with something for everyone from the commercial superstore to small businesses like Ma Doughty's record store.

The multi-screen movie theatre is a hit, particularly with the civilian population, especially when it shows the live broadcasts of the Saturn Saturday Night Spectacular. On the far side of the building is the music hall where music lovers can enjoy regular concerts performed by many of the most talented musicians on the scene.

The Comm-Sat Cafe provides patrons with an opportunity to relax, unwind and enjoy a delicious selection of treats and beverages. The establishment also boasts the greatest number of public videophones in the whole Space City complex.

An olympic-sized swimming pool, indoor running track and fully equipped gymnasium round out the amenities on offer in Block Charlie. The pool is especially popular as the crystal clear water provides a refreshing and welcome contrast to the desert landscape on the surface.

VENUS'S BEACH HOUSE

Venus owns her very own beach house on the north coast of the island, a few kilometres from the residential apartment block. The beach house is situated beside the waves of Otello beach and affords Venus the perfect location to get away from it all and relax in her off-duty time.

While the outside of the property looks rather ordinary, Venus was reluctant to part with many of her 21st-century comforts so the interior of the house features a wide array of hi-tech gadgets.

Chief among these is Venus's pride and joy, her hi-fi system and large collection of discs which she adores listening to alone or with company. A set of amplifiers and variable-brightness lighting panels help transform the personal space into a far-out listening lounge.

The innovations don't end there. Venus also has an alarm service that wakes her up in the morning and automatically opens the blinds to let the dawn light in.

Although constructed from a prefabricated shelter designed for colonists, Venus later made some changes with the help of Steve Zodiac and Professor Matic. The trio added a spiral staircase leading to an observation deck which gives fantastic 360 degree panoramic views of the landscape.

The beach house was destroyed during a space emergency in 2063, but with the help of the Space City construction crew it was rebuilt to be exactly the same in every detail as it was before.

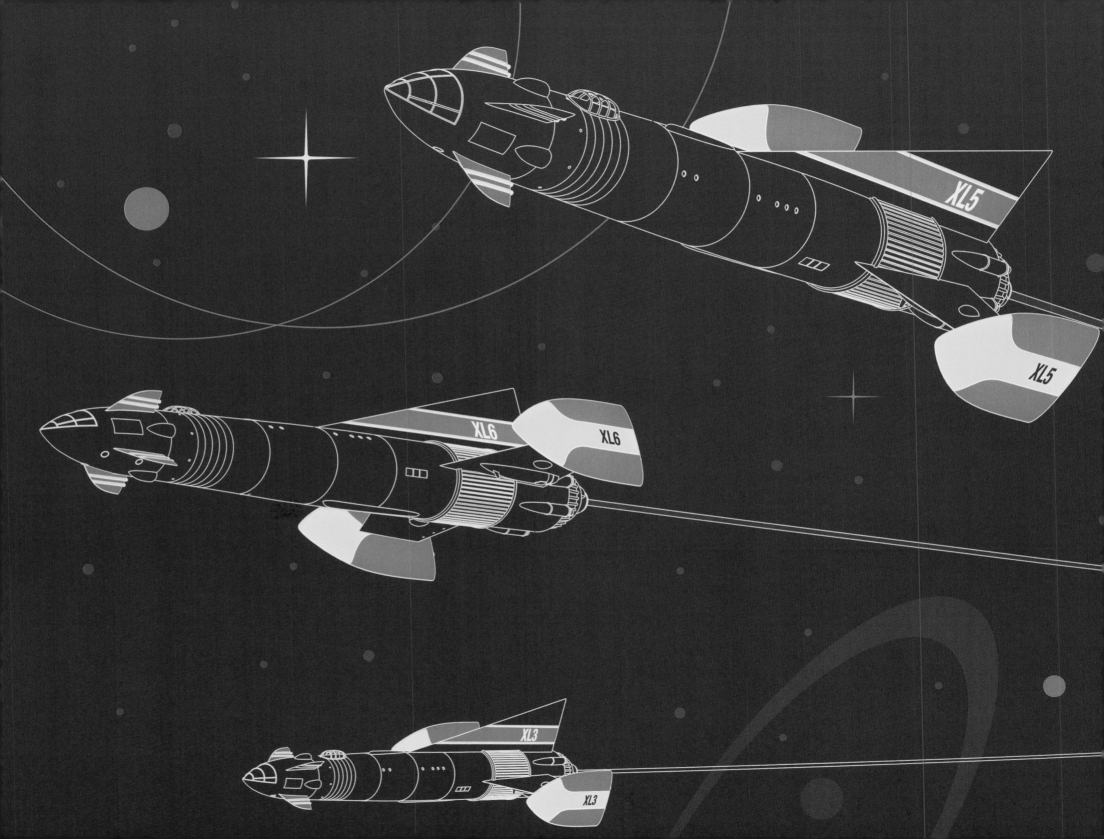

Section 2

FIREBALL CRAFT

XL-CLASS PATROL SHIP

The creation of the WSP fundamentally changed humankind's perception of space. Instead of being a vast unknown expanse to be explored, it became the new frontier, settled by people from all walks of life who were dependent on a fragile logistical network to keep them supplied.

The organisation needed a new ship, one that could be equally suited to charting space, carrying supplies or going into combat. Using the ageing TA-series of explorer vessels as its starting point, the best minds in the WSP across the globe set to work designing the ship, developing and acquiring new technologies to create something leagues ahead of anything that had come before.

As an initial testbed for these new technologies, the Century 21 (C21) was designed to test the nutomic drive that had been developed to enable the craft to fly at interstellar speeds. The craft completed its first flight circumnavigating the sun in less than an hour, however, deficiencies in the hull led to an excess thermal discharge from the reactor. As a result, the reactor dangerously overheated and nearly led to the loss of the craft. This close call led to a new heat-resistant material being developed from a Cahelium-X extract. The C21 was permanently mothballed, but the accident led to a new nickname for the project, "Fireball".

With the drawbacks of the prototype C21 addressed, Fireball XL1 exceeded almost every expectation and nine more were immediately commissioned to form the first wave of patrol ships to enter service. At present 30 XL-class patrol ships form the Fireball fleet, with another wave currently under construction.

SYMBOL OF PROTECTION

The Fireball fleet has grown to become the most iconic element of the WSP for many alien civilisations and humanity in general. For the vulnerable, they have become a symbol of protection. And for those that threaten galactic peace, the harbingers of justice. The design has become so versatile and adaptable that there are currently no plans to replace the fleet. Instead, remedial servicing keeps the craft operational, with larger refits and modernisation scheduled for every tenth year of each vessel's operational lifetime.

Fireball Craft

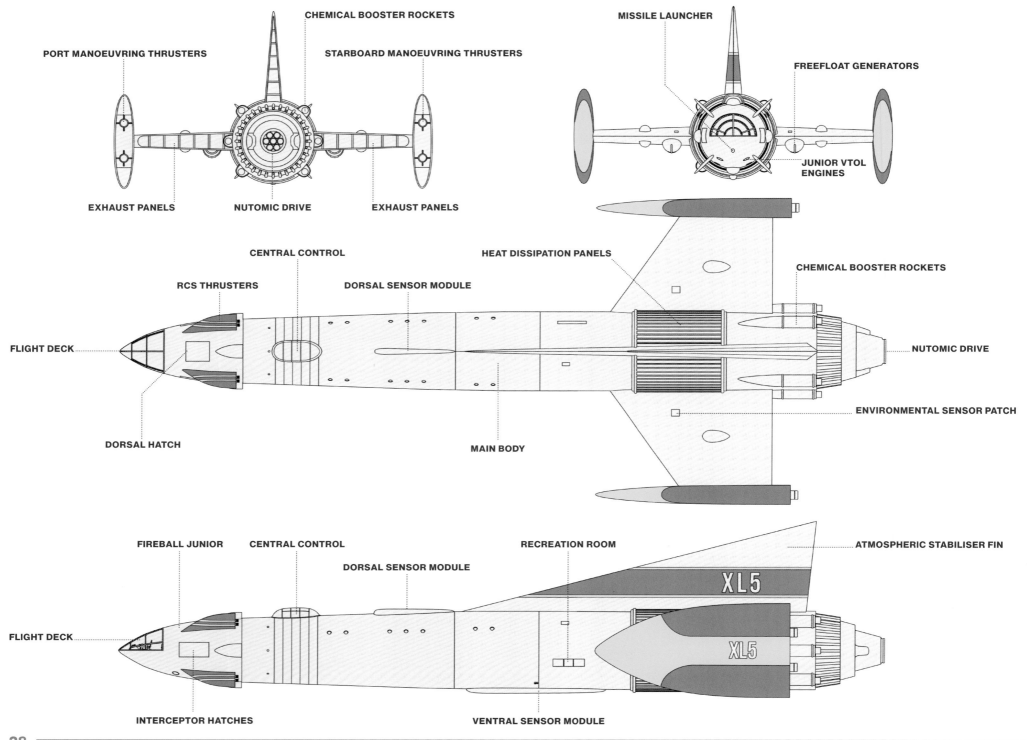

CHEMICAL BOOSTER ROCKETS

PORT MANOEUVRING THRUSTERS

STARBOARD MANOEUVRING THRUSTERS

MISSILE LAUNCHER

FREEFLOAT GENERATORS

JUNIOR VTOL ENGINES

EXHAUST PANELS

NUTOMIC DRIVE

EXHAUST PANELS

CENTRAL CONTROL

HEAT DISSIPATION PANELS

CHEMICAL BOOSTER ROCKETS

RCS THRUSTERS

DORSAL SENSOR MODULE

FLIGHT DECK

NUTOMIC DRIVE

DORSAL HATCH

MAIN BODY

ENVIRONMENTAL SENSOR PATCH

FIREBALL JUNIOR

CENTRAL CONTROL

RECREATION ROOM

ATMOSPHERIC STABILISER FIN

DORSAL SENSOR MODULE

XL5

FLIGHT DECK

XL5

INTERCEPTOR HATCHES

VENTRAL SENSOR MODULE

FLEET IDENTIFICATION

Externally, XL-class patrol ships are made from the same Cahelium-X extract reinforced hull across the whole fleet. Some vessels, such as the Space Rescue series or XL craft with an experimental drive or an enhanced sensor suite, will feature a subtly different livery behind the Fireball Junior's docking collar in order to help identify specifically adapted craft. Three blue stripes signify a standard Fireball, three red stripes a Space Rescue craft, three yellow stripes a designated interceptor vessel, and a chequered yellow and black pattern signifies an experimental testbed.

CONCEALED ARMAMENTS

In order to provide the best profile for interstellar speeds, much of Fireball's external equipment is secured beneath hatches on the hull and stowed away during flight. Chief among this is the formidable arsenal of weapons. Located on either side of Fireball Junior are two banks of interceptors – variable yield, guided missiles – that are specifically used to attack moving targets in space. At a low yield, these can be set to non-lethally cripple a target, while on higher yields a single missile can completely obliterate an enemy vessel and anything else in its immediate vicinity. Interceptors can be swapped out for air-to-ground missiles at Space City should the need arise.

A smaller unguided missile launcher is fitted to the prow of Fireball Junior for close-quarter engagements.

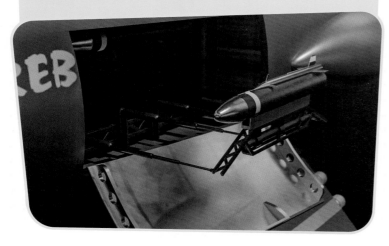

INTERNAL LAYOUT

An XL-class patrol ship is designed to support a crew of four for a three-month tour of duty. For this reason, the craft is full of amenities spread over two decks including science labs, workshops, a generous cargo bay and some communal living space. Most Fireballs will launch with this standardised layout, but this may be altered over time in order to specialise the craft for specific mission profiles.

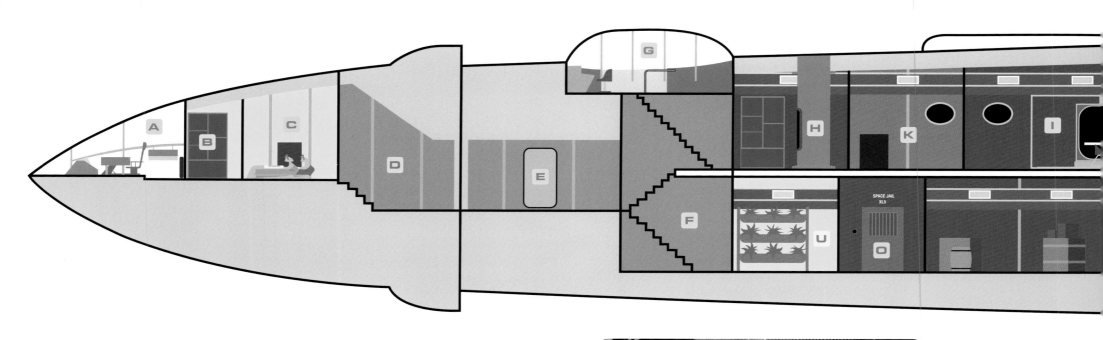

A **Flight deck** (page 34)

B **Junior aft compartment with supplies and fold-down bunk space**

C **Equipment storage and airlock**

D **Junior access corridor**

E **Main body docking corridor and airlock**

F **Stairwell and access to central control**

G **Central control** (page 36)

H **Ejection room** (page 37)

I **Navigation bay** (page 38)

J **Ladder access to B deck**

K **Access corridor**

2

L (Starboard) Medical laboratory

M (Port) Engineering laboratory

N Cargo bay

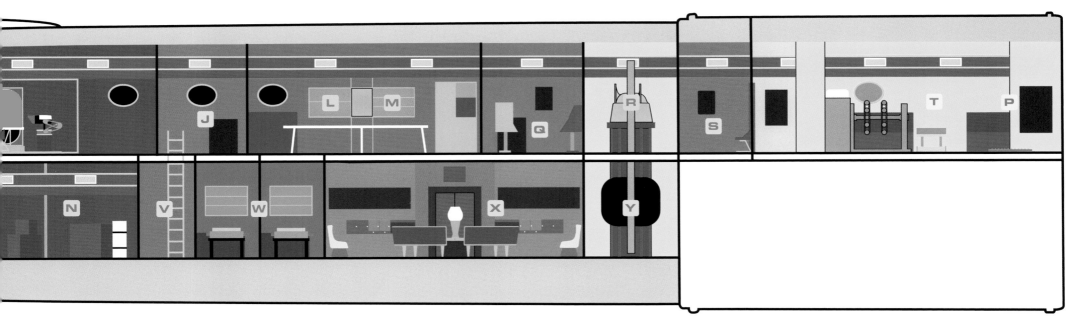

O	Jail cell	R	Space gyro (page 43)	V	Ladder access from A deck
P	Access to reactor maintanence walkway	S	Auxiliary control	W	Living quarters
Q	Engineering decontamination section	T	Nutomic reactor room (page 43)	X	Recreation room
		U	Hydroponic storage	Y	Space gyro, B deck

FIREBALL JUNIOR

When operating in deep space, your vessel is your most valuable asset and placing it in harm's way is deemed an unacceptable risk. In order to maximise the capabilities of the XL-class patrol vessel, a solution was required to mitigate this risk.

Fireball Junior is the name given to the detachable command module of an XL-class patrol vessel. It was decided early in the design process that in order to maximise the amount of time the ship could remain on patrol, only the nose cone would separate to make planetfall. This approach resulted in a tremendous amount of energy saved as the entire vessel would not need to enter and leave a planet's atmosphere on a regular basis. It also allows an additional degree of safety by leaving the craft's main body in orbit where the remaining crew can oversee the landing area and either call for assistance or render aid in an emergency.

The Fireball Junior module incorporates the front two compartments of the Fireball and is not designed for long trips. Much of the aft space is used to store Jetmobiles and other landing party-specific equipment. The large red fins incorporate the Fireball's forward RCS thrusters making Fireball Junior extremely manoeuvrable and much more adept than the main body at exploring and landing on difficult terrain. With a small amount of preparation the vehicle can even travel underwater.

The two sections are unified by a series of magnetic clamps which guide the craft in for docking. To separate the craft, the polarity of the magnets is reversed, pushing Fireball Junior clear and allowing its engines to fire without damaging the docking mechanisms. In situations where the ship may need to dock with another craft, the docking magnets can secure the back of the ship to the metallic hull of another vessel and a boarding tube can be extended to create an atmospheric seal.

EXTREMELY RESISTANT

As the nose cone of the entire vessel, in addition to its Cahelium-X hull, Fireball Junior has been reinforced to withstand the force of interstellar travel. This makes the craft extremely resistant to damage in perilous conditions, such as extreme atmospheric pressure, molten rock or even direct strikes by meteorites. Despite this, the hull is not invulnerable and is difficult to repair in the field so astronauts must be careful to keep the craft out of harm's way whenever possible.

FLIGHT DECK

At the dawn of spaceflight, an astronaut would have been lucky to have a tiny porthole through which to view the Earth and navigate their vessel. By contrast, at the very front of the Fireball is the XL patrol ship's panoramic flight deck.

With its transparent viewports offering a completely unobstructed view of space, from here, two astronauts can pilot the vessel while maintaining regular communication with the navigation bay.

At first glance, one might be struck by how simplistic the controls are with a yoke, pedals, a side console and a series of readouts displayed on the console in front of the pilots. This is partly the result of several control systems being linked into the master computer. For instance, the yokes are tied directly into the space gyro, which syncs up the reaction control wheels and thrusters to allow the whole ship to quickly and efficiently react to the pilot's input. The pedals control boosters and retro rockets while the side consoles allow the control systems to switch between different modes of operation.

These control systems seamlessly transfer over when the Fireball Junior module is detached from the main body, however, the pilot will have to bear in mind that the significantly different centre of mass will change the attitude of the craft.

In circumstances where a crash is imminent and preclude detaching Fireball Junior, the entire windshield can be separated and the flight chairs expelled in a similar manner to conventional ejector seats.

LAYOUT CONFIGURATION

The layout of an XL-class's flight deck may change depending on crew preference. Most Fireball's sport the standard two-person design, while some may only utilise one flight console. Others may change the location of the side consoles or add a third station towards the back of the room on the port side.

WINDSCREEN

The massive windscreen of the Fireball could be considered a design flaw as most of the force of travelling at interstellar speeds will act on this very section. However, the screen is coated in the same Cahelium-X extract as the rest of the craft making it as strong as any other part of the ship. It has proven vulnerable to weapons fire in the past, most notably when an Aquaphibian attacked Fireball XL5 Junior in 2063. Professor Matic developed a chemical coating that offers an additional degree of protection, but similar threats are not to be underestimated.

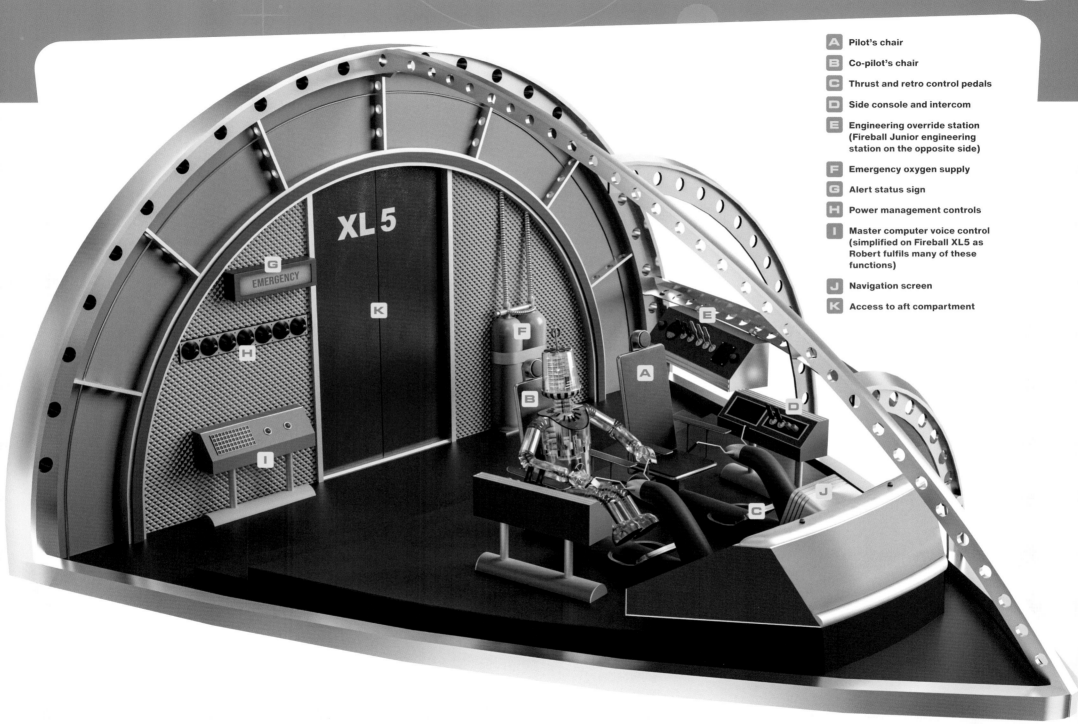

A   Pilot's chair

B   Co-pilot's chair

C   Thrust and retro control pedals

D   Side console and intercom

E   Engineering override station
(Fireball Junior engineering
station on the opposite side)

F   Emergency oxygen supply

G   Alert status sign

H   Power management controls

I   Master computer voice control
(simplified on Fireball XL5 as
Robert fulfils many of these
functions)

J   Navigation screen

K   Access to aft compartment

CENTRAL CONTROL

Located in the front section of the main body of the XL craft is central control, a dome-type structure that allows the craft to be manually piloted when Fireball Junior has been detached.

It is a relatively small space with room for two and the master control console at the front, plus a retractable ladder allowing access and empty space towards the aft. This additional space allows for telescopes and other astronomical sensors to be set up for research purposes.

A Retractable access ladder

B Master control console

C Fireball Junior override console

D Pilot's chair

E Co-pilot's chair

F Observation area

G Environmental unit

SECONDARY CONTROL

Should the main flight deck be destroyed and the primary flight crew lost, then the navigator can use central control to assume command of the ship and pilot it to safety. As a further backup, a secondary control station is located near the Fireball's engine room that allows simple programmed commands to be issued.

PROFESSOR MATIC

Being the oldest member of the Fireball XL5 crew, Professor Matic will often remain on board and control the main body from orbit either by himself in central control or with Robert. Depending on what happens on the ground, he can either land to render aid or move the main body of the ship to safety.

EJECTION ROOM

Aft of central control is the ejection room – a small room loaded with equipment that astronauts might require on a spacewalk or exploring other zero gravity environments.

Instead of a traditional airlock, a crewmember will enter the ejection chamber which will quickly depressurise and release them into space, where their thruster pack will automatically engage and allow them to hover in place.

An equipment locker on the far wall contains a supply of radios, equipment belts, coma rays, oxygen pills and magnetic boots.

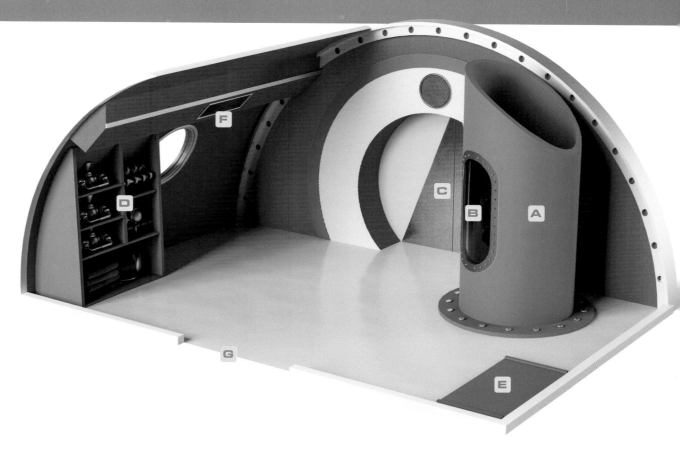

A Ejection tube (offset to port to prevent astronauts from being struck by the tail fin in flight)

B Glass door

C Access to navigation bay

D Equipment locker

E Equipment locker

F Ventilation system

G Access to central control and Fireball Junior

CARGO RAMP

While the ejection tube allows for a quick and efficient way to leave the craft, there are two other ways to leave an XL ship. Located under the vessel with direct access to the ship's cargo bay, the cargo ramp can deploy in either a slope or staircase configuration to allow the crew to load the vessel or disembark if the main body has landed on an alien world.

FIREBALL JUNIOR HATCH

The main exit for the ship's complement of Jetmobiles is located above their storage bay on Fireball Junior. A hatch can open allowing for entrance and exit. The dorsal placement of the hatch makes it more difficult for hostile entities to gain entry to the vessel.

NAVIGATION BAY

The centre of the vessel is arguably the brains of the ship – the navigation bay. A large room spanning the width of the ship, it holds an extensive library of star charts as well as interfaces for the Fireball's main computer, and controls for the retractable optical and radio telescopes.

From here, the ship's navigator can use these assorted resources to accurately map the vessel's location and chart courses that are both fuel efficient and free of navigation hazards.

NAVIGATOR'S DESK

The navigator's desk is a large 300-degree arc that can rotate to face either of the two main screens used for displaying star charts on each side of the room. A third screen, which displays images from the onboard telescopes, is mounted on the desk platform so that it can rotate along with the desk itself, enabling the navigator to compare the chart and telescope images. Printed charts will often be used for marking up and plotting. The chair can be raised and lowered for the navigator's comfort.

EXTRA CONSOLES

In addition to navigation, the resources of the navigation bay can be vital for accurately aiming the ship's weapons systems when a target is in range. Two extra consoles are mounted to the main desk: one can override the interceptor controls on the flight deck and allow the weapons to be pre-programmed for maximum accuracy; while the other ties into the control frequencies of the interceptors and can override potential jamming signals.

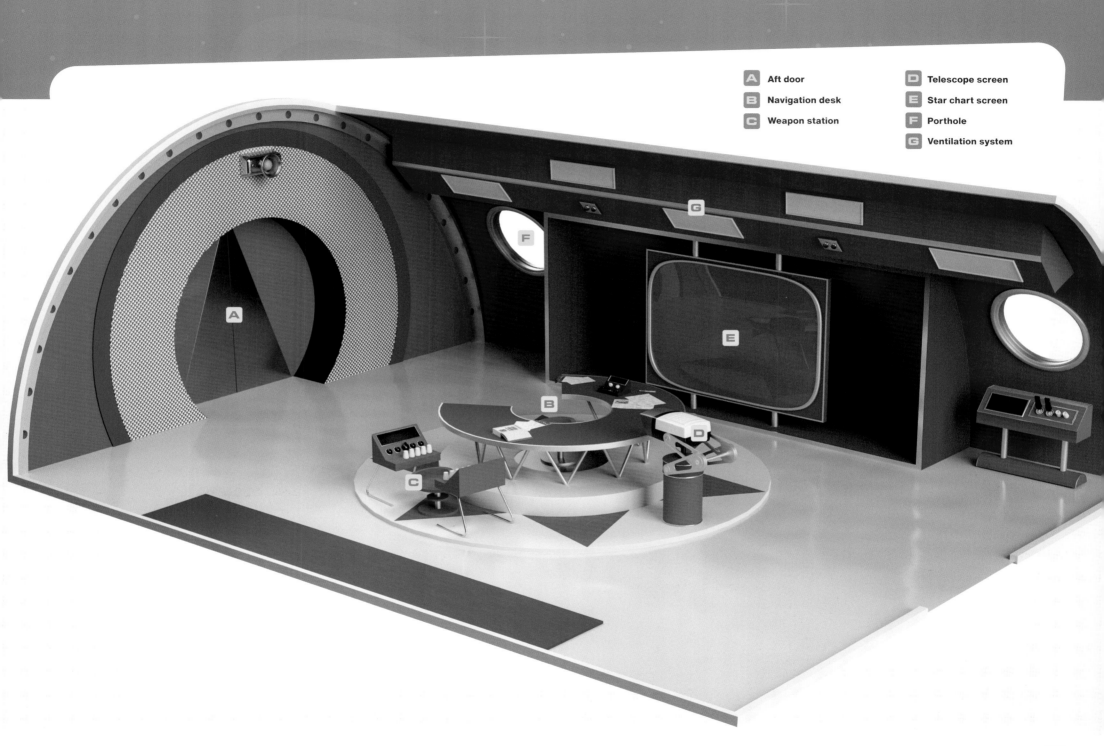

LIVING AREAS

A standard patrol for a Fireball can last from three months to as much as a year when on extended assignment. For this reason it is important that areas of the ship are reserved for the crew to relax and unwind while off duty.

THE LOUNGE

The lounge is the main communal space and will often be subtly different across each vessel as the crews tailor it to their purposes. In general, two curved sofas wrap around a central table while two units stocked with books, magazines and games dominate the largest wall. Unusually, instead of the regular portholes located on the ship, a large rectangular window allows for a panoramic view of space. This reduces the claustrophobic feeling of being on board a spacecraft for long periods of time. In times of crisis the window can be covered by a retractable blast shield.

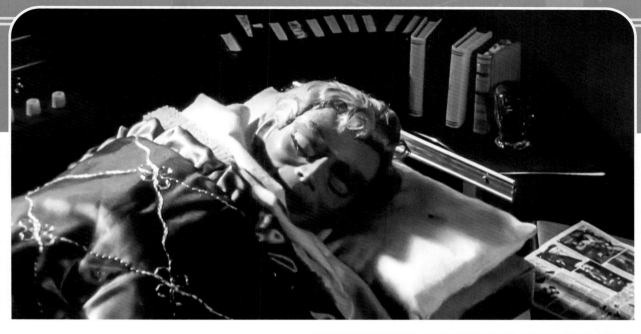

CREW QUARTERS

An XL-class vessel allows space for four sets of living quarters. These small areas are actually housed within a single compartment with removable soundproof partitions that allow their layout to be changed. On Fireball XL5, for example, the fourth crewmember – Robert – is a robot who does not require quarters, so Doctor Venus has been allocated the additional space.

Quarters, most often, will comprise a single or double bed, a wraparound shelf for personal items, a wardrobe, a sink and an intercom unit. A communal bathroom is located along the corridor.

A Central table (a tea and coffee dispenser is concealed underneath the lamp and can be accessed at the touch of a button)

B Artwork unique to each Fireball

C Entrance

D Additional seating for passengers or diplomatic functions

E Clock and intercom speakers

F Main seating area

PRISON

As part of their role as an interstellar patrol craft, the situation may arise where a Fireball will be required to take on prisoners for secure transport to Earth to await trial. For this reason, the XL-class is equipped with a rudimentary prison cell. This spartan room has a reinforced steel door, and features a bed and a retractable sink and toilet.

As this room is adjacent to the cargo bay it may sometimes be used for additional storage.

ENGINEERING SECTION

Located towards the aft of the craft is the engineering section, notable by the ring of radiator panels surrounding the hull. This section contains the nutomic reactor, space gyro, nutomic fuel and other important electronic components vital for running the ship.

As the most dangerous area of the vessel, it is specially shielded to prevent any radiation leakage or in the worst case, to direct the force of a nutomic explosion towards the aft of the vessel, increasing the chances of the crew's survival. This entire section is also detachable allowing the nutomic drive to be removed and worked on or replaced with other experimental drives.

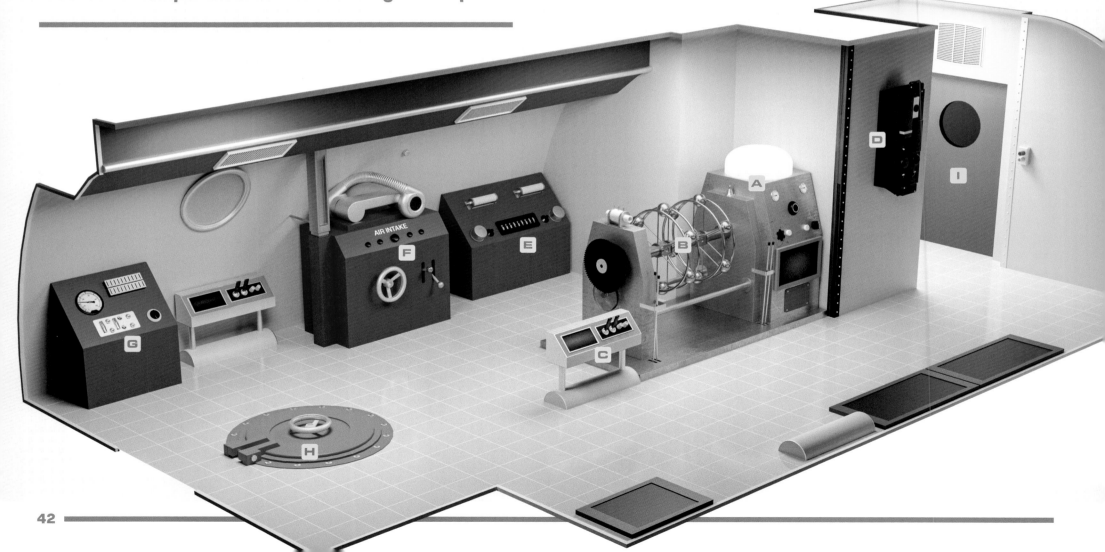

PROTECTIVE SUITS

While usually safe to enter, during times of high power output by the nutomic reactor, background radiation in this section can rise to dangerous levels. In these instances, the crew will be expected to don protective clothing and eyewear, and take anti-radiation pills until the section can be decontaminated.

SPACE GYRO

The space gyro sits at the forward end of the engineering section and serves two main functions. Firstly, it is a component of Fireball's navigation system allowing the orientation of the craft to be calculated in relation to the galactic plane. Secondly, it is a component of Fireball's reaction control system. Two wheels, one positioned around the gyro itself and one located on board Fireball Junior, allow the craft to turn without needing to use its manoeuvring thrusters.

NUTOMIC REACTOR ROOM

The nutomic reactor room is the largest part of the engineering section and is located above the reactor itself with its manual control rods and secondary turbines. Other important components can be accessed through this room, such as life support systems, power regulation and artificial gravity.

A   Nutomic reactor controls

B   Secondary energy turbines

C   Comms system

D   Power regulation controls

E   Emergency batteries

F   Air supply controls

G   Artificial gravity controls

H   Access to maintenance walkway below

I   Entrance and access to space gyro

SPACE RESCUE 1 AND 2

There are two additional craft stationed at Space City that use XL-class hull configurations: Space Rescue 1 and Space Rescue 2.

The Space Rescue variants are identical to their XL counterparts externally, bar a different colour scheme. They have the same engines, are equipped with Fireball Juniors and are armed with space interceptor missiles.

However, unlike the other XL craft, the Space Rescue vessels are fitted out with a comprehensive array of life-saving and repair equipment. Most of the internal areas dedicated to exploration and planetary studies have been replaced with hospital bays and triage supplies. The cargo bay and communal areas have also been stripped out and instead contain a repair bay with two large double doors evocative of early space shuttle designs.

In an emergency situation, a Space Rescue craft is designed to take a position above a stricken vessel and open its large repair bay doors. Inside are various manipulator arms capable of holding craft in place and welding hull breaches closed, as well as additional fuel, fire suppressant and oxygen supplies that can be connected accordingly.

In even more desperate situations, such as an out-of-control reactor, the Space Rescue craft can use a cutting laser to shear off the habitable areas of a spacecraft and carry it to safety.

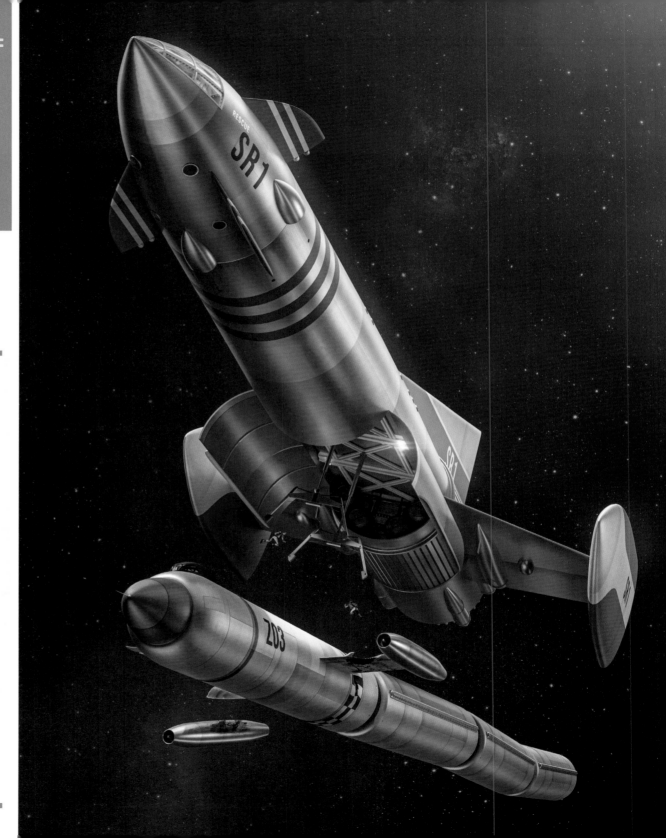

HANGARS

Space Rescue 1 is kept ready for action in a dedicated Rescue Hangar bay above ground, close to the main apron of the Space City control tower. This allows the craft to be immediately scrambled into action at a moment's notice. When an emergency call requiring immediate action is received, the code call, "Emergency Red – Code 24, Go!" will be broadcast from the main operations room and Space Rescue 1 will proceed to the launch rail and be lifted into position by the launch rail cranes.

Space Rescue 2 is kept in readiness in XL Hangar 1 below the surface and can be raised to the Rescue Hangar on a lift platform. This is done immediately when Space Rescue 1 has cleared the launch rail so that Space Rescue 2 is instantly ready for any further emergency calls that may arise.

COMMANDER ZERO

With a background in Space Rescue, Commander Zero is the de facto commander of Space Rescue 1 unless he is otherwise required at Space City, with Lieutenant Ninety acting as co-pilot when required. Like a regular Fireball, the flight deck can be quickly modified for use by one or two pilots. An additional crew of doctors and rescue specialists will also be rapidly embarked, ready to render aid in an emergency situation.

RESCUE 1

- **COMMANDER:** Commander Jonathan Wilbur Zero
- **ADDITIONAL CREW:** Lieutenant Josef Ninety
- **STATUS:** Active, ready for launch at Space City

RESCUE 2

- **COMMANDER:** Major Pierce Dalton
- **ADDITIONAL CREW:** Lieutenant Judi Lee
- **STATUS:** Active, searching Sector 17 for XL26

LAUNCH RAIL

Designed for the sole purpose of facilitating the launch of XL-class spaceships, this twin-rail platform runs due west from Space City and ends in a curved incline two kilometres from the main complex.

The launch process commences when a Fireball is raised from the subterranean hangar bay to the surface on the platform situated behind the launch rail.

A pair of gantry cranes on the starboard side of the rail raise the XL craft up off the platform and carry it to the launch rail, where a launch sled is ready and waiting on the end of the rail. The spacecraft is lowered onto the sled and secured for ignition. Once the fuelling procedure has been completed, the fuelling gantries are retracted and any additional cargo is loaded aboard from a hydrocrane on the port side of the craft.

STAGE 2
When launch clearance has been given, the pilot remotely fires the launch sled's primary solid rocket boosters and the XL craft gathers speed as it is propelled along the launch rail.

STAGE 1
Stage one, the crew perform final preflight checks and secure the ship's contents for take off. The tower completes a final radar sweep to ensure local air traffic is clear and gives launch clearance.

2

The launch rail incorporates a powerful arresting clamp that is used when an XL craft needs to perform a static test of its motors. With the clamp securely in place, the spacecraft can safely throttle up its motors to full power and back down again without moving from the start of the rail.

Although the launch rail has proven its worth time and time again saving valuable fuel that would otherwise be wasted by vertical take offs, reliance on a single launch rail has occasionally been problematic. As of mid-2063, a second launch rail is in the planning stages and, once completed, will be positioned parallel to the original on the far side of Space City.

STAGE 4

The Fireball races up the incline and activates its nutomic drive while decoupling from the launch sled, which drops down onto the recovery track to begin the journey back to the start of the launch rail.

STAGE 3

As the launch sled builds speed, the secondary solid rocket boosters fire, doubling the craft's acceleration.

LAUNCH SLED RETURN SYSTEM

Once an XL craft has departed the launch rail, the launch sled motors cut out and it drops down onto a recovery rail. The recovery rail banks sharply downward to the left, which swiftly takes the sled underground and back on a parallel course with the launch rail. Here, it joins a line of spent launch sleds that are checked over, refuelled and certified for use again. When a launch sled is required, a platform raises the next available sled to the surface, where it is lifted onto the launch rail by the gantry cranes. It remains in position ready to receive the next XL craft and begin the launch cycle again.

FIREBALL XL0

- **STATUS:** Decommissioned
- **NOTES:** Formerly known by the designation Century 21. Prototype of the XL-class now preserved as a museum exhibit at Unity City's aerospace heritage pavilion

FIREBALL XL1

- **COMMANDER:** Captain John Maxwell
- **ADDITIONAL CREW:** Lieutenant Judith Read
- **STATUS:** Active, assigned to Space City as relief craft
- **NOTES:** Originally known as Fireball XL1-Alpha, this vessel was the first production-specification XL craft to be built after the XL0 prototype. Although considered to be outdated compared with later vessels in the line, XL1 remains an important testbed for new technology, such as refinements to the nutomic motors and the emergency ejection system

FIREBALL XL2

- **COMMANDER:** Captain Ken Johnson
- **ADDITIONAL CREW:** Lieutenant Al Stomper
- **STATUS:** Destroyed by space monster on planet Monotane, crew rescued

FIREBALL XL3

- **COMMANDER:** Colonel Conrad Turner
- **ADDITIONAL CREW:** Lieutenant Jeremy Dean
- **STATUS:** Active, patrolling Sector 27

FIREBALL XL4

- **COMMANDER:** Captain Jason Knoll
- **ADDITIONAL CREW:** Lieutenant Otis Hackbart, Doctor Chloe Quasar
- **STATUS:** Active, assisting with major refit of Space Station 5

FIREBALL XL5

- **COMMANDER:** Colonel Steve Zodiac
- **ADDITIONAL CREW:** Doctor Venus, Professor Matthew Matic, Robert the Robot
- **STATUS:** Active, patrolling Sector 25
- **NOTES:** Due to its distinguished service record and widespread fame, XL5 is considered to be the flagship of the WSP fleet

FIREBALL XL6

- **COMMANDER:** Lieutenant Reg Meddings
- **ADDITIONAL CREW:** Doctor Penelope Thamm
- **STATUS:** Active, patrolling Sector 8

FIREBALL XL7

- **COMMANDER:** Lieutenant Robert Ross
- **ADDITIONAL CREW:** Lieutenant Chuck Traeger
- **STATUS:** Destroyed, forcibly scrapped on planet Magneton, crew rescued

FIREBALL XL8

- **COMMANDER:** Captain Erin Summers
- **ADDITIONAL CREW:** Lieutenant Chuck Morrison
- **STATUS:** Destroyed by cosmic colossus, crew rescued

FIREBALL XL9

- **COMMANDER:** Lieutenant Stuart Wyngarde
- **ADDITIONAL CREW:** None
- **STATUS:** Damaged in sneak attack by S.S. *Thor*, under repair at Space City

FIREBALL XL10

- **COMMANDER:** Colonel Nick Nebula
- **ADDITIONAL CREW:** Professor Brie Pluto, Doctor George Bishop
- **STATUS:** Active, escorting diplomatic convoy to Astran Peace Summit

FIREBALL XL11

- **COMMANDER:** Captain Nicole Davison
- **ADDITIONAL CREW:** None
- **STATUS:** Missing, contact lost while patrolling Sector 20

FIREBALL XL12

- **COMMANDER:** Captain Sam Taylor
- **ADDITIONAL CREW:** Lieutenant Bill Chesterfield
- **STATUS:** Active, patrolling Sector 16

FIREBALL XL13

- **COMMANDER:** Captain Willow Smith
- **ADDITIONAL CREW:** Lieutenant Glenn Tracy
- **STATUS:** Active, patrolling Sector 5

FIREBALL XL14

- **COMMANDER:** Colonel Mike Sullivan
- **ADDITIONAL CREW:** Lieutenant Frank Noble, Doctor Leanne Kyte
- **STATUS:** Active, extended duration mission mapping the Seahorse Nebula

FIREBALL XL15

- **COMMANDER:** Colonel Karen Taggart
- **ADDITIONAL CREW:** Lieutenant Paul Floyd, Professor Arnold Langston
- **STATUS:** Active, undergoing engine upgrade at Mars Station

FIREBALL XL16

- **COMMANDER:** Colonel Shane Zimmerman
- **ADDITIONAL CREW:** Lieutenant Peter Graham, Lieutenant Ray Holliday
- **STATUS:** Self-destructed to prevent alien invasion fleet from reaching Earth, crew rescued
- **NOTE:** XL16 is the only vessel of its class to be lost due to use of the self-destruct system

FIREBALL XL17

- **COMMANDER:** Captain Hector Sanchez
- **ADDITIONAL CREW:** Lieutenant Juliette Lynch
- **STATUS:** Active, searching Sector 20 for XL11

FIREBALL XL18

- **COMMANDER:** Lieutenant Jack Flanagan
- **ADDITIONAL CREW:** None
- **STATUS:** Destroyed while investigating gaseous anomaly approaching Earth, crew lost
- **NOTES:** Prior to its destruction, XL18 was being used as a test craft for the new ultra long-range space tracking system

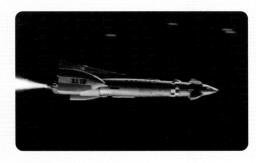

FIREBALL XL19

- **COMMANDER:** Colonel Brian Samuel
- **ADDITIONAL CREW:** Lieutenant Genevieve Culshaw, Lieutenant Justin Forester, Doctor Anna Jameson
- **STATUS:** Active, crew on shore leave to planet Olympus

FIREBALL XL20

- **COMMANDER:** Colonel Chris Robinson
- **ADDITIONAL CREW:** Lieutenant Glynn Thompson, Professor Thomas Knox
- **STATUS:** Active, investigating reports of alien fleet massing in Sector 26

FIREBALL XL21

- **COMMANDER:** Captain Laura McGill
- **ADDITIONAL CREW:** Lieutenant Stefan Bronson
- **STATUS:** Missing, contact lost while studying black hole in Sector 9

FIREBALL XL22

- **COMMANDER:** Lieutenant Sara Coral
- **ADDITIONAL CREW:** None
- **STATUS:** Active, undergoing space trials after recent refit

FIREBALL XL23

- **COMMANDER:** Lieutenant Jill Marsh
- **ADDITIONAL CREW:** Lieutenant Ace Owens
- **STATUS:** Damaged by giant space gorilla on planet Foresta, under repair at Space City

FIREBALL XL24

- **COMMANDER:** Captain Richard Dale
- **ADDITIONAL CREW:** None
- **STATUS:** Destroyed while investigating gaseous anomaly approaching Earth, crew lost

FIREBALL XL25

- **COMMANDER:** Lieutenant Evie Bennett
- **ADDITIONAL CREW:** Lieutenant David Gordon
- **STATUS:** Active, Fireball Junior undergoing prolonged subaquatic tests

FIREBALL XL26

- **COMMANDER:** Captain Patrick Steed
- **ADDITIONAL CREW:** Lieutenant Samantha Rigg
- **STATUS:** Missing, contact lost while investigating space warp in Sector 17

FIREBALL XL27

- **COMMANDER:** Colonel Carl Ramsey
- **ADDITIONAL CREW:** Lieutenant Geoff Wilson, Professor Bill Wade, Doctor Jerome Singh
- **STATUS:** Damaged by coma cannon fired from planet Zavia, currently undergoing repairs at Space City

FIREBALL XL28

- **COMMANDER:** Colonel Zarrene Mercury
- **ADDITIONAL CREW:** Lieutenant Harry Masters
- **STATUS:** Active, on special training manoeuvres with Space Fleet Delta

FIREBALL XL29

- **COMMANDER:** Colonel Guadalupe Armendáriz
- **ADDITIONAL CREW:** Lieutenant Bradley McClaine
- **STATUS:** Active, patrolling Sector 12

FIREBALL XL30

- **COMMANDER:** Colonel Lars Gruber
- **ADDITIONAL CREW:** Lieutenant Kestra Jackson, Doctor Earl Fredrickson
- **STATUS:** Active, assisting with terraforming operation on planet Exodon

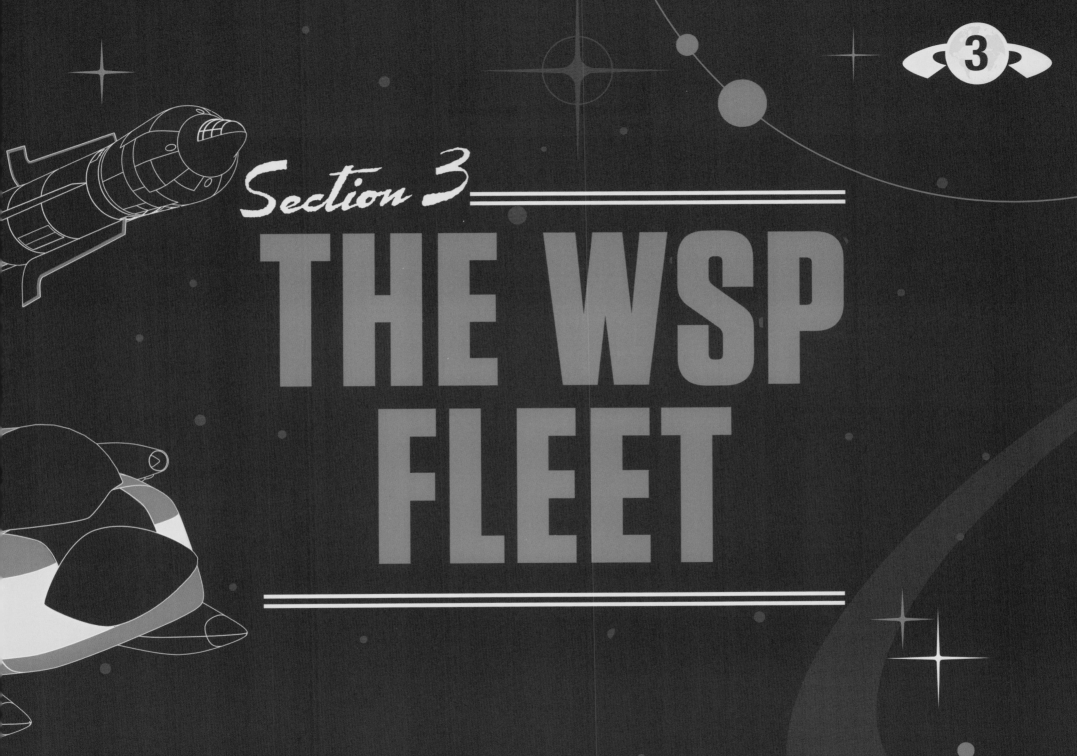

Section 3

THE WSP FLEET

THE MARVEL OF THE AGE!

INTRODUCTION

While the XL-class of space vessel is the most visible of the WSP's fleet, it is only the spearhead of a large number of support craft.

Designed to fulfil a range of tasks such as logistics, science and defence leaving the Fireball fleet to patrol and explore the universe. Many of these craft are a common sight across Space City's launch pads while others have been relegated to the Aeronautics and Space Museum at Unity City.

A budding astronaut will usually have to build up flight hours on several different vessels before being put in command of a prestigious XL craft.

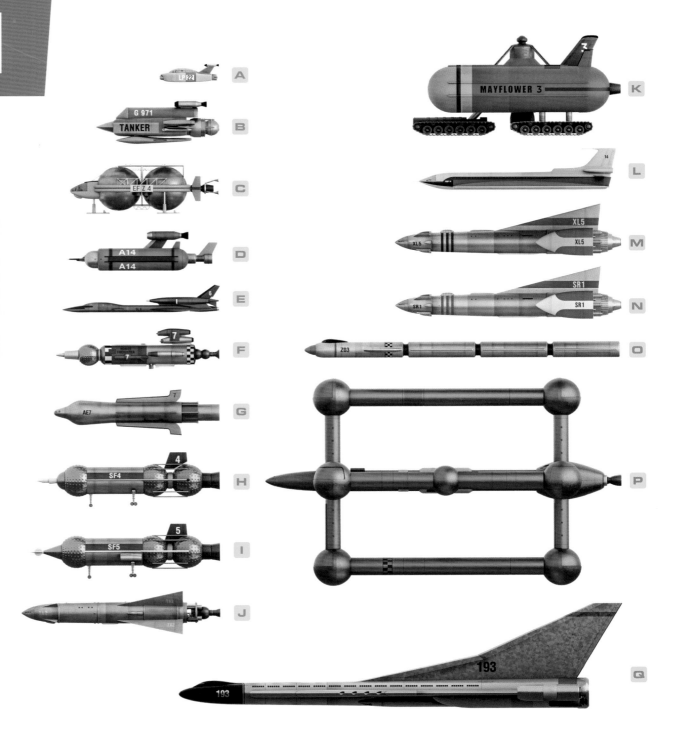

A	Light Patrol Craft – 24m	**I**	Q-Ship – 75m
B	G-Type Tanker – 50.5m	**J**	TA-Class Explorer – 81.5m
C	E-Type Tanker – 60m	**K**	Mayflower Colony Ship – 84m
D	A-Type Freighter – 62m	**L**	VTOL Transport – 85m
E	Supersonic Airliner – 64m	**M**	Fireball XL-Class – 91.5m
F	Robot Freighter – 67m	**N**	Space Rescue Craft – 91.5m
G	Expedition Craft – 68m	**O**	Space Train – 128m
H	Liberty-Class Space Freighter – 74m	**P**	Space Battleship – 146m
		Q	Interstellar Liner – 180m

LIGHT PATROL CRAFT

The Light Patrol Craft (LPC) is a smaller vessel when compared to other WSP spacecraft. However, it is fast, manoeuvrable and can pack a reasonable punch when pitted against a regular pirate marauder.

The sector of space surrounding Earth is mainly patrolled by the Fireball fleet. However, the expensive nature of the craft means there are only a limited number in service. These gaps have not gone unnoticed and are frequently exploited by pirates or hostile alien powers to infiltrate worlds, smuggle contraband and attack shipping. In response, the WSP commissioned a new type of craft that can operate from a space station or colony to patrol trade routes and local space, allowing the larger vessels to focus on deep space.

While it does have a faster-than-light drive, its range is limited and so an LPC will most commonly operate within the solar system in which it is based.

COCKPIT

Given the small size of the LPC, crews are generally limited to one or two astronauts, with a standard patrol lasting no longer than a week. A large glass canopy across the generously sized flight deck allows the pilot an unrestricted and spectacular view of space around the craft. A ladder leads to the deck below which houses the living quarters and engineering section. LPCs are generally commanded by a master astronaut or sub-lieutenant.

CANOPY

Rather than possessing a traditional airlock, the LPC's canopy opens up, allowing the pilot to leave the craft either by thruster pack or retractable ladder if the LPC has landed on a planet.

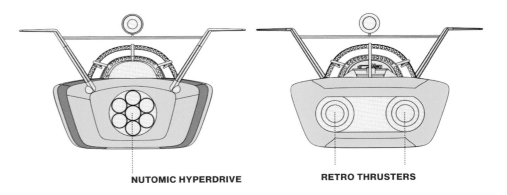

NUTOMIC HYPERDRIVE

RETRO THRUSTERS

A FORCE TO BE RECKONED WITH

While the small profile of the LPC may not seem imposing to an armed pirate vessel, the craft's speed and agility, coupled with a battery of unguided missiles, makes the LPC a real force to be reckoned with. Though not quite as prestigious as operating a Fireball, LPC crews need to have an equally expert mastery of their vessel in order to use its abilities to their advantage – a direct missile strike would likely destroy the craft.

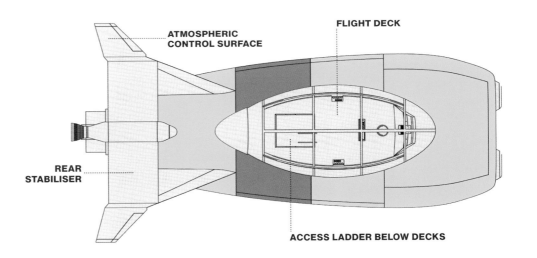

ATMOSPHERIC CONTROL SURFACE

FLIGHT DECK

REAR STABILISER

ACCESS LADDER BELOW DECKS

SUBLIGHT ENGINE

RETRO THRUSTERS

LANDING MANOEUVRE

Another impressive feat of the LPC is its ability to make landfall on planets. Because of the impact on fuel, it can perform this manoeuvre only a few times on each patrol and therefore a pilot will need to make a judgement call on whether landing is absolutely necessary. Three landing legs support the craft when on the ground.

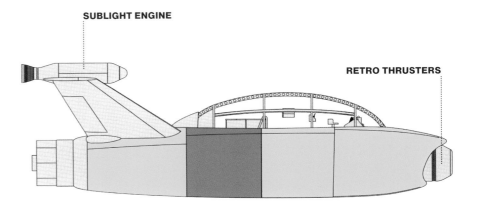

TA SERIES EXPLORATION CRAFT

The TA series of survey ships represented the first wave of humankind's efforts to explore the universe. First launched in 2010, decades before the formation of the WSP, these ships were primarily responsible for mapping solar systems and scoping out planets for future vessels to make a landing on.

The TA series used atomic motors that were considered vastly outdated in comparison to the newly developed nutomic hyperdrive. This meant that the craft needed to be optimised for long-haul flights with a crew generally limited to one or two depending on the duration of the mission. For this reason, pilots were selected for their aptitude, facility to deal with solitude and their ability to improvise without the aid of a team. Upon their return, many of these pioneers were revered internationally and played a key role in forming what the WSP would become.

Only one ship of the class, the TA4, survives in preserved condition today. It is currently located close to the XL0 at Unity City's aerospace heritage pavilion.

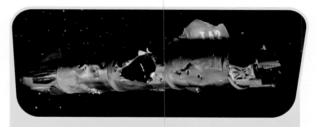

COLONEL HARRY DENTON

The most famous example of a TA craft is the TA2 commanded by Colonel Harry Denton. Following a successful series of missions charting Sector 24, the TA2 vanished without trace. For years its fate remained unknown until the crew of Fireball XL5 stumbled upon the wreckage abandoned in deep space. Clues left behind by Colonel Denton led XL5 to the planet Arctan where Denton was found alive and well, having become a benevolent ruler over the peaceful inhabitants.

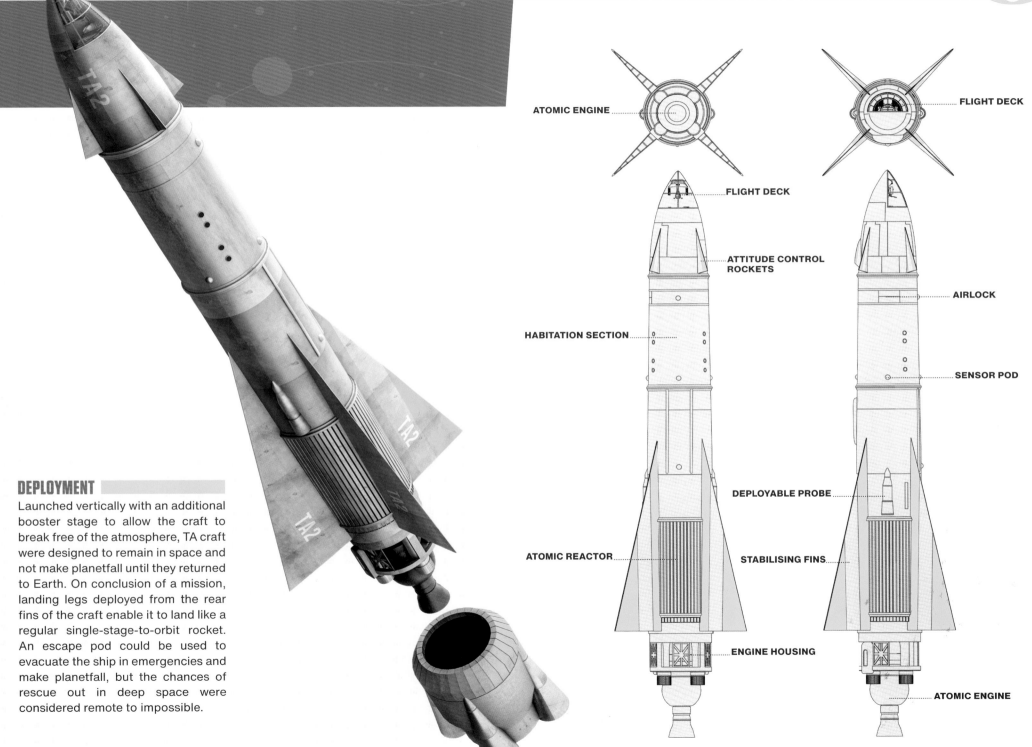

3

ATOMIC ENGINE

FLIGHT DECK

FLIGHT DECK

ATTITUDE CONTROL
ROCKETS

AIRLOCK

HABITATION SECTION

SENSOR POD

DEPLOYABLE PROBE

ATOMIC REACTOR

STABILISING FINS

ENGINE HOUSING

ATOMIC ENGINE

DEPLOYMENT

Launched vertically with an additional booster stage to allow the craft to break free of the atmosphere, TA craft were designed to remain in space and not make planetfall until they returned to Earth. On conclusion of a mission, landing legs deployed from the rear fins of the craft enable it to land like a regular single-stage-to-orbit rocket. An escape pod could be used to evacuate the ship in emergencies and make planetfall, but the chances of rescue out in deep space were considered remote to impossible.

SPACE BATTLECRUISER

Following several successive alien attacks at the heart of the WSP, it became apparent that Earth's defences were woefully inadequate and that the Fireball fleet was too widely dispersed across the galaxy to protect home space. A mothballed design from the 2050s was quickly updated and mass-produced in order to fill this gap.

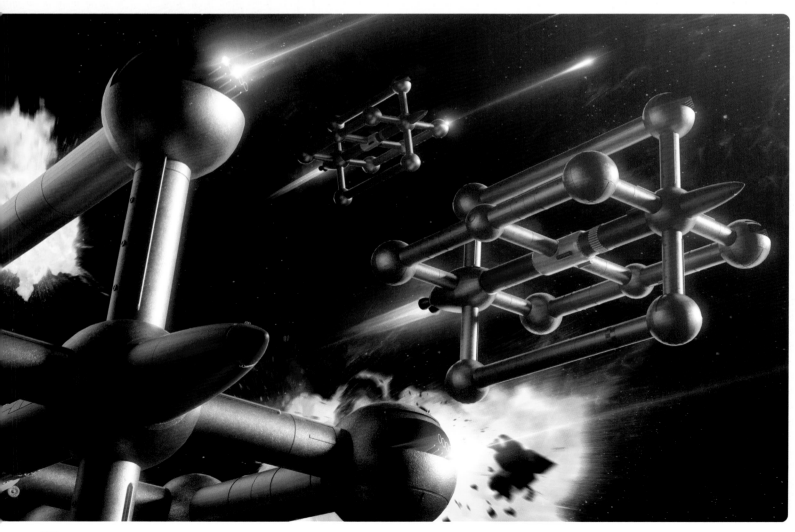

The Space Battlecruiser is a modular design consisting of a central core that houses the command module, reactor and engines, and a superstructure that allows eight turrets to be mounted around the craft. This simplistic design allows a lot of versatility and customisation across the fleet, with different vessels swapping out the turrets for alternate weaponry, sensor pods or other mission-specific equipment.

Each Space Battlecruiser is manned by 22 personnel who operate in a zero-g environment in order to more easily navigate the unusual design of the craft.

Currently, there are four fleets in the WSP's defence force – Alpha, Beta, Gamma and Delta – that patrol deep within Earth space. Following a disastrous encounter with the Astran Defence Force, new laws and regulations have been drafted limiting the area these fleets can operate in unless the situation is deemed to be an emergency.

TURRETS

Learning from flaws within the naval battleships of the Second World War, the eight turrets are spaced out sufficiently that in the event that one is destroyed, it won't compromise the integrity of the rest of the craft. The most common loadout for a Space Battlecruiser is four interceptor launchers on the vertical axis and four mass accelerator turrets on the horizontal axis.

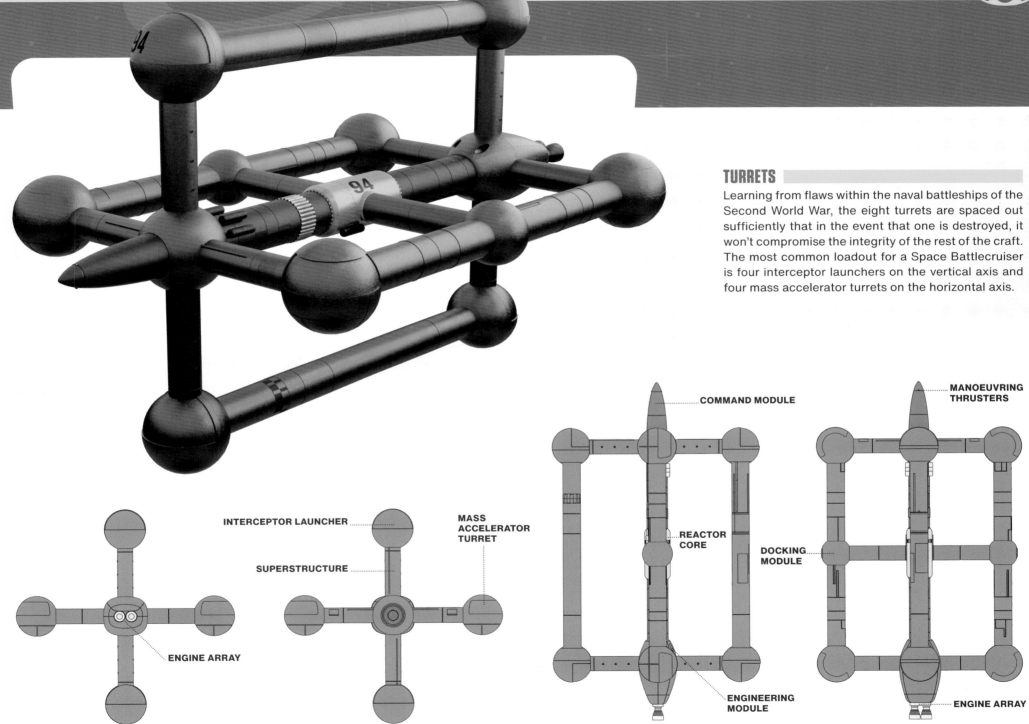

SPACE Q-SHIP

In 2062, with levels of piracy becoming untenable, Space City refitted a number of Liberty-class space freighters, reinforcing their superstructure, installing additional engines and outfitting their lower cargo bay with interceptor banks.

With an increasing need to supply colonies and outposts across Earth's space, newly assigned "space lanes" were quickly swamped with hundreds of cargo vessels bound for destinations in almost every direction. These lightly-armed and slow-moving vessels became obvious targets for interstellar pirates and hostile alien powers. While valuable freight shipments are often escorted by LPCs or even Fireball vessels on occasion, the WSP was quickly spread too thin to be on hand every time a freighter sent out a distress call.

The exact number of Q-Ships in service and the routes they follow is classified in order to allow them to function effectively, ensuring potential attackers can never be certain their prey is not a predator in disguise.

INTERIOR

The interior of a Q-Ship is functionally quite similar to a standard freighter with some additional surplus control equipment from an XL-class flight deck. The upper cargo bays have been left unmodified in order to allow the vessel to continue to operate as a freighter. For this reason, the Q-ships are manned by experienced freighter crews with additional combat training.

LIBERTY-CLASS FREIGHTER

To the untrained eye, the Q-Ship is almost identical to the standard Liberty-class freighter, but a seasoned space captain will notice the additional side-mounted boosters and an advanced sensor system attached to the nose cone of the vessel. These features are only apparent when the vessel is in visual range and well within firing distance of the craft's interceptor banks.

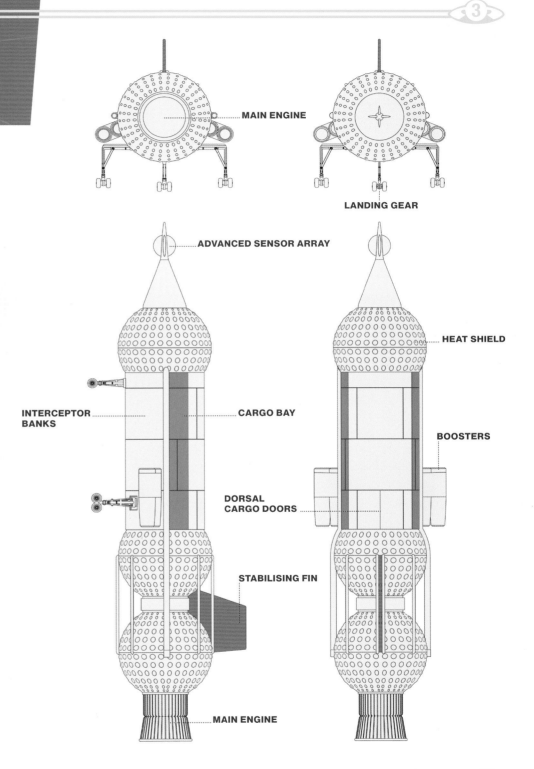

MAIN ENGINE

LANDING GEAR

ADVANCED SENSOR ARRAY

HEAT SHIELD

INTERCEPTOR BANKS

CARGO BAY

BOOSTERS

DORSAL CARGO DOORS

STABILISING FIN

MAIN ENGINE

MAYFLOWER CLASS COLONY SHIP

Operated by the Space Immigration Organisation, the Mayflower series of colonisation ships were developed to aid the goal of terraforming new planets and creating new human colonies on otherwise barren worlds.

Modular in construction, these craft are designed to ferry colonists and equipment to their new world, and eventually be disassembled to form the primary power plant and structures of a fledgling colony. If the world's atmosphere and gravity are not immediately suitable for habitation, atmospheric generation units and gravity densification systems can be deployed to terraform the planet with crews relying on oxygen pills and "lead boots" in the interim.

As the Mayflower series is unarmed, a Fireball will usually scout ahead to ensure the planet is safe and remain in the vicinity during the initial set-up of the colony.

FLIGHT DECK

Like many civilian and logistical craft used by the WSP, the Mayflower's flight deck features a simplistic design, operated by one or two crew members during flight. Many of the more complex tasks are preprogrammed into the craft's onboard computer.

COLONY SHIP

A Mayflower will make many return trips to Space City in order to acquire all the raw materials required for the initial colony construction. The upper levels that form the cargo bay are loaded by cranes while colonists embark via ladder to their cabins on the lower levels.

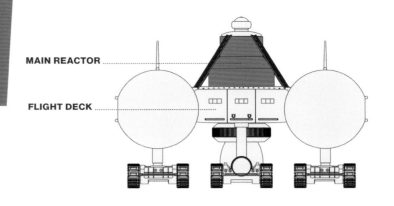

MAIN REACTOR

FLIGHT DECK

PORT TRANSPORT POD

CONTROL AND ENGINEERING SECTION

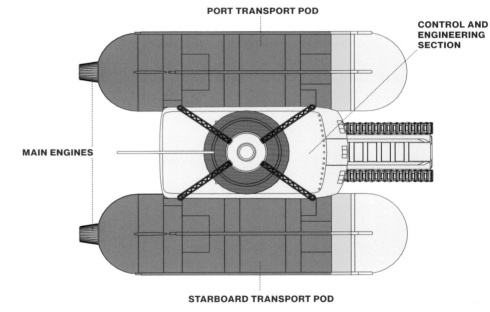

MAIN ENGINES

STARBOARD TRANSPORT POD

MODULAR CONSTRUCTION

The unconventional shape of the Mayflower revolves around its ability to be disassembled and repurposed into whatever the colony requires. The main reactor takes the form of a prefabricated building and can be disconnected from the top of the craft and lowered onto the surface with ease to form the colony's power source.

In a similar vein, the tracked mobility system on each of the landing legs can be removed to form a small fleet of ancillary vehicles.

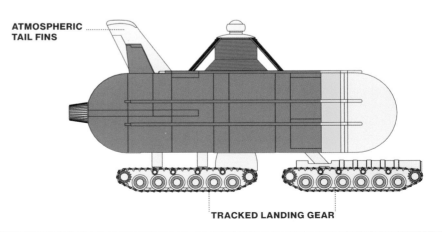

ATMOSPHERIC TAIL FINS

TRACKED LANDING GEAR

ATMOSPHERIC TRANSPORT

While the WSP operates many interstellar craft that can fly hundreds of kilometres per second in space, a series of terrestrial aircraft are also used to facilitate the movement of equipment and personnel around Earth itself. Specifically designed to operate efficiently within Earth's atmosphere, there are two common variants.

VTOL TRANSPORT

The VTOL transport is a modified civilian airliner which makes up the primary shuttle service to the Space City atoll. With the standard model capable of carrying up to 100 passengers, the WSP variant has been retrofitted to carry 40 in a comfortable business lounge-style cabin. If an emergency evacuation is required, the maximum passenger capacity can be increased to 60.

What makes the VTOL transport particularly remarkable is its unusual wing configuration. Instead of being used to generate lift like a regular aircraft, a gravity repulsor system similar to the "free-float" technology used on XL craft keeps the liner in the air while its main engines can accelerate the aircraft to Mach 16. As a security measure following the threat of Bereznik and SOFRAM terrorist attacks, the VTOL transport has been armed with low yield air-to-air missiles.

SUPERSONIC MILITARY AIRLINER

A more traditional aircraft than its civilian counterpart, the SL-type airliner has a proven track record as a safe and reliable VIP transport plane, being shortlisted as a possibility for the new "World Air Force One".

The aircraft is designed around a traditional supersonic frame with two wing-mounted jet engines and a central ramjet that operates in flight. For take off and landing, a standard runway is most commonly used, however, the craft is able to achieve vertical take off by rotating its two jet engines into VTOL position. The SL can carry two pilots and a maximum of 10 VIPs.

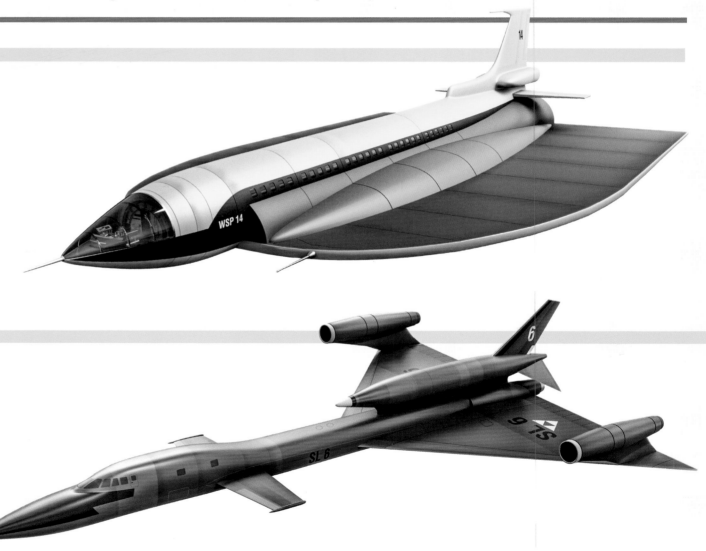

SL-TYPE AIRLINER INTERIOR

As a military aircraft, the interior is designed with practicality in mind. Given the status of the VIPs on board, however, some attempts have been made to make the passenger cabin more luxurious. Due to the craft's incredible speed, it is unlikely that anyone would spend more than an hour on board before disembarking.

ASSASSINATION ATTEMPT

Recently, the SL6 was involved in a Subterrain plan to kill General Rossiter by hypnotising its pilot, Major Todd, to crash the aircraft into the Space City control tower. Luckily, Doctor Venus, who was also on board, was able to subdue Major Todd and take control of the aircraft, bringing it to a safe landing.

SUPPORT CRAFT

In addition to the WSP's primary fleet, a wide variety of support craft are required to keep all of Earth's spacecraft, space stations and colonies supplied and running efficiently. These vessels account for the bulk of spacecraft that use Space City's facilities on a daily basis.

E-TYPE TANKER

The E-type tankers are easily identifiable by their rounded hulls, fuelling ports and standard space-code hazard markings, and will most often be used to move fuel to space colonies that are unable to refine their own. Regulations governing the approach and departure of tankers from any of Space City's landing pads are strictly observed at all times. There is always the possibility of a fire or explosion when dealing with large quantities of flammable material, so every precaution is taken to mitigate these risks.

G-TYPE TANKER

The G-type tanker is a smaller fuel tanker, faster and hardier than its E-type counterpart. It has been specifically designed to resupply spacecraft in the field and as such it is also equipped with a limited rescue capability.

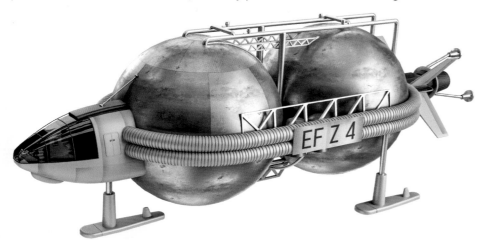

COCKPIT

The E-type tanker cockpit is split into two sections, a forward manual control area and an aft standing console that controls the onboard computer. Given the extremely volatile nature of the cargo, the onboard computer will most often be used to fly the ship with a single pilot on board to monitor the craft.

TAKE OFF

As G-type tankers have been in service for many years, a great deal of diversity can be seen across the class – particularly with the older models. This example has been modified with pontoons in order to make a water landing on the planet Hydrar.

LIBERTY-CLASS SPACE FREIGHTER

The standard and most commonly seen type of freighter across Earth space, the Liberty-class were mass-produced in the 2040s when it became clear that humankind had expanded its reach too fast and was struggling to supply its frontier colonies. Named after its World War II counterpart, the Liberty-class is a bare-bones spacecraft still possessing many outdated features such as a heat shield and magnetic floors. A modernisation project has been undertaken to start updating the Liberty-class to current safety standards.

ROBOT FREIGHTER

With many spacecraft largely being run by computer control, it became clear that a completely robotically operated freighter was an increasingly viable prospect. These advanced crewless vessels are flown by a master computer guidance unit and can be configured to transport a host of different cargo depending on the mission parameters. The automated nature of the craft means that skilled crews can be assigned to more vital duties rather than having to pilot low-priority freight runs.

Q-SHIPS

The Liberty-class makes up a large proportion of the total vessels seen across the space lanes, and their dated state makes them a tempting target for pirates and foreign powers looking to steal equipment or ore. Although Space City has started operating a series of Q-ships to mitigate this threat, some space captains have begun arming their own Liberty-class ships in an effort to tip the balance in their favour.

STEALING CARGO

While the automated nature of the freighter makes it the perfect choice to move cargo around the safer regions of Earth's space, the process isn't completely infallible. Freighters can break down, making them easy targets for salvagers, while there have also been instances of people illegally reprogramming freighters to either deliberately damage them or steal their precious cargo.

SPACE TRAIN

The Space Train is a high-speed freighter with a series of modules connected in sequence behind the main drive section of the craft. Often these are designed to make large bulk deliveries to newly established colonies after their Mayflower craft has been disassembled. The Space Train can also be reconfigured to carry prefabricated space station components that can be quickly assembled at the required destination.

INTERCEPTOR MISSILES

Given that the Space Train will often be required to travel into areas of unregulated space without an escort, banks of interceptors can be deployed from its drive section. These banks are orientated to the port and starboard of the craft as the Space Train's payload would make precise manoeuvring in a combat scenario extremely difficult.

A-TYPE BULK FREIGHTER

The A-type Bulk Freighter is heavier and more robust than the standard Liberty Freighter containing two large cargo modules at each side of the craft. Unlike other freighters, these cargo bays are designed to be loaded separately and then quickly attached to the drive section of the craft. This means that loading can be done before the craft's arrival and cargo modules can be quickly swapped, allowing for a swift departure.

TRAFFIC CONTROL

A-types are a common sight at Space City as a popular supply vessel for off-world WSP bases. The expeditious nature of their arrival and departure requires traffic control crews to be extra careful in order to prevent a collision between them and other vessels.

SCHEDULED PASSENGER SERVICE

A common sight in the skies above Earth are the space liners operated by the World Spaceways Organisation. These craft can hold up to 1,000 passengers and crew on flights that generally last up to a day.

Space City is a predominantly government-run facility and, as such, it does not operate the same variety of civilian passenger services as commercial spaceports. However, it does operate two of these craft on the regularly scheduled overnight trip to Mars. Each day, a single transport ship departs Space City bound for the red planet and one vessel makes the inbound journey in return. The service is frequented by civilians and administrative staff from the Martian colonies visiting relatives based at Space City and vice versa. The continued operation of this overnight ferry service generates a modest source of additional income for the WSP.

TERMINUS SPACE STATIONS

As space liners operate with limited range, terminus space stations have been set up in deep space between solar systems. These stations function much like airports back on Earth and allow passengers to disembark and transfer onto other flights or stay overnight.

EXPEDITION CRAFT

While Fireballs will often act as the vanguard of humanity's space exploration programme, more specialised Expedition craft will often be used to follow up on important discoveries or to ferry scientific personnel out to previously unexplored worlds.

Smaller than the Fireball XL ships, these craft are generally unarmed but well-stocked with supplies for long-haul missions, with advanced communication and sensor equipment plus additional cargo space to bring samples back to Earth.

ASTRONAUT TRAINING

While being assigned an Expedition craft could be seen as a "babysitting exercise" for up-and-coming astronauts, these missions will often face unique challenges that require crew to quickly adapt on the fly. Unfortunately, many of these ships have been lost or have gone missing under mysterious circumstances.

SPACE STATIONS

While setting up bases on habitable planets has become the preferred method of creating permanent infrastructure in space, a large number of satellites and space stations have been constructed across Earth-occupied space in order to fulfil a variety of tasks.

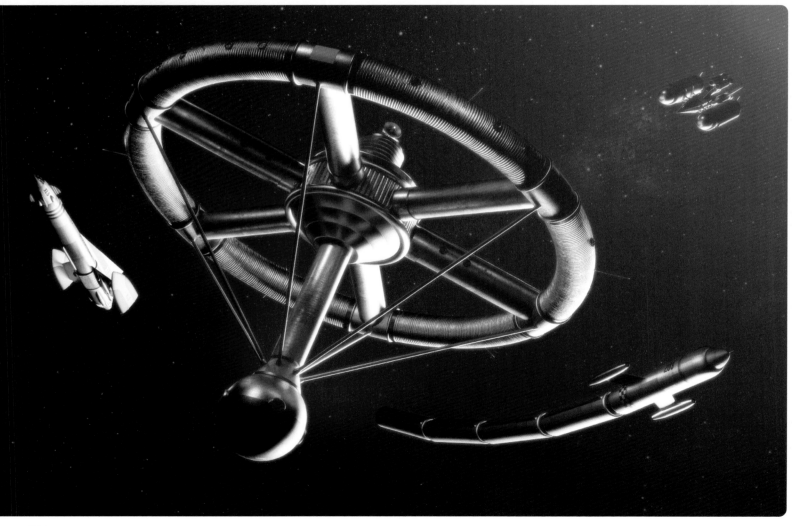

COMPANION STATIONS

A large bulk of the stations in service are the Companion-class stations. First assembled across the perimeter of Earth-occupied space in the 2040s, these stations fulfil several key functions:

- As markers denoting the edge of Earth's space and monitoring the presence of potentially hostile vessels breaching that space.

- As fuel depots and refineries allowing vessels to refuel and restock without having to make a fuel-intensive landing on a planet.

- As mobile command posts allowing flag officers to oversee operations from a secure location.

- **A** Primary antennae
- **B** Habitat ring
- **C** Reactor module
- **D** Central control
- **E** Superstructure supports
- **F** Running lights

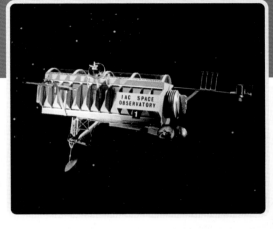

SPACE OBSERVATORIES

Space Observatories are specially designed outposts used to monitor deep space away from the potentially disruptive effects of a planet. Various antennae monitor for radio or neutroni signals, while other experimental technologies, such as the "Ultrascope", can provide direct images of the surfaces of distant worlds.

COMPANION 12

Companion 12, named after the 12 nations that funded its construction, is the oldest of the Companion series of stations and marks the old perimeter of Earth space as it was in the 2040s. Currently used as a waypoint and refuelling depot for XL craft, it is scheduled for demolition and replacement in 2068.

SKYBALL 1

The WSP has become universally renowned for its engineering prowess in designing and constructing complicated spacecraft and stations to tackle specific problems. For example, when a highly combustible gas cloud threatened Earth, the crew of Fireball XL5 were able to repurpose and deploy the mothballed "Skyball 1", a large satellite, to trap and safely detonate the cloud.

INTERIOR

Being much older than regular WSP designs, the interiors of these Companion stations are much less luxurious than their modern counterparts. Additionally, they do not possess artificial gravity and require magnetic boots to safely walk their corridors.

Section 4

EQUIPMENT

INTRODUCTION

While the members of the WSP receive some of the highest levels of training in order to prepare them for whatever they may face in the depths of space, it is also vital that they are equipped with the most advanced and reliable equipment available.

To this end, the research and development team at Space City are constantly devising new forms of field equipment. Additional equipment is obtained by reverse engineering advanced alien technology that is acquired during trade or recovered during missions.

This section will cover the various forms of field equipment that are stored on board the Fireball fleet and will instruct you on their use. Read carefully, as on the frontier, your wits and equipment will be the only things that stand between you and the threats of outer space.

RADIO

Potentially the most vital piece of equipment in an astronaut's arsenal, this advanced form of radio allows crews to stay in contact with each other over long distances.

Essentially a scaled-down version of the Neutroni transmitter installed on board a Fireball, this handheld version allows for instantaneous communication at a range of almost 1 million kilometres. It is unaffected by most materials and is powerful enough to act as an emergency signal to flag down passing spacecraft during an emergency.

A	Microphone/Speaker
B	Antennae
C	Volume
D	Frequency
E	Push to talk

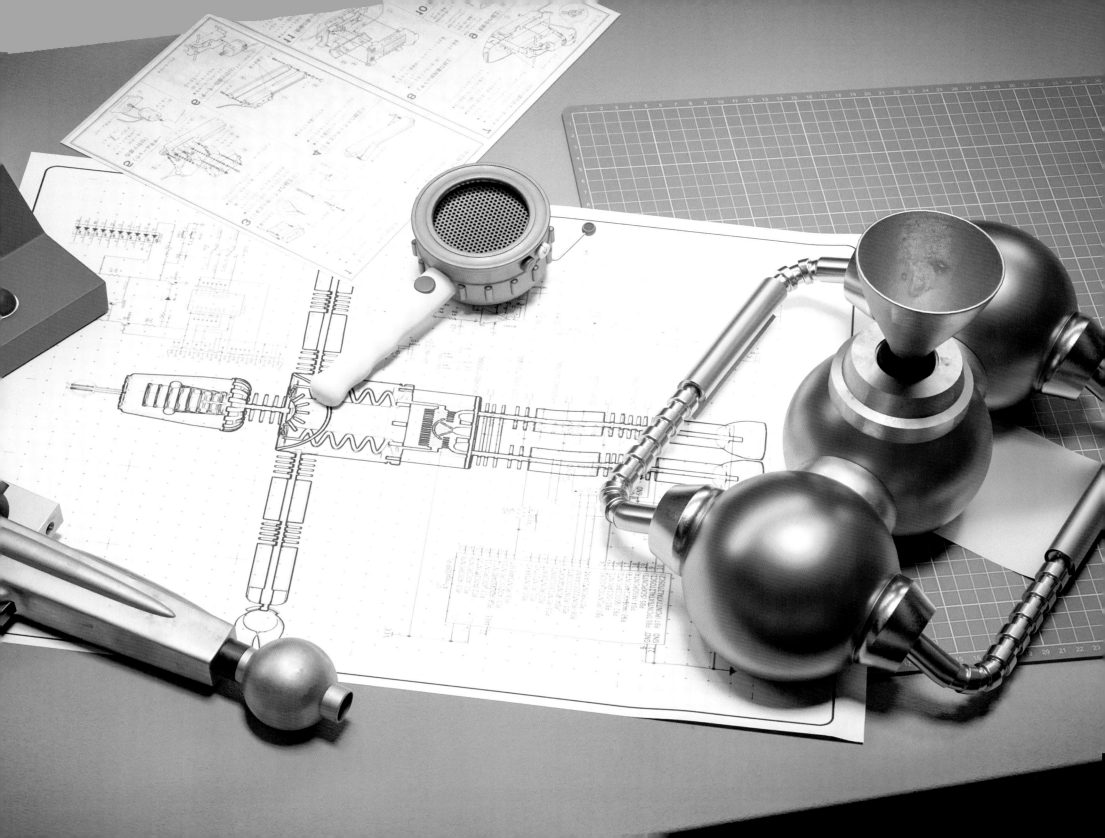

UNIFORMS

Where humans once ventured into space wearing bulky protective gear, the modern astronaut is now kitted out in a much more comfortable and aesthetic work uniform. These uniforms are designed to be practical for the needs of the wearer while also making members of the WSP distinct from the other branches of the world's forces.

ASTRONAUT

The standard astronaut uniform consists of a grey jacket with an exaggerated red collar and cuffs, grey trousers, a pale yellow undershirt adorned by a patch signifying their posting and weather-resistant tan boots. Junior astronauts may have a darker grey or brown jacket while master astronauts will have pips on their epaulettes.

MEDICAL STAFF

Medical staff are provided with a more practical uniform that features a green coverall to make them both easy to identify and to replace and wash following medical emergencies or experiments. Beneath this, they wear a grey shirt with red cuffs, and grey trousers with green boots in a similar style to the astronauts.

ENGINEERS

Rather than wearing a uniform while doing intensive maintenance work, many of the engineers will be seen wearing protective coveralls that can easily be replaced and washed. This relaxed uniform code is only in effect outside of important command visits or diplomatic situations.

FREIGHTER CAPTAINS

Freighter crews and other merchant vehicles will often don a similar uniform to other support crews, though when on assignment captains may decide to take a more relaxed approach between ports.

SUPPORT STAFF

Mostly worn by ground support staff at installations such as Space City, the support uniform is more simplistic than the astronaut uniform consisting of a brown and tan jacket with tan trousers. The lieutenant variant features additional black epaulettes which coil at the end.

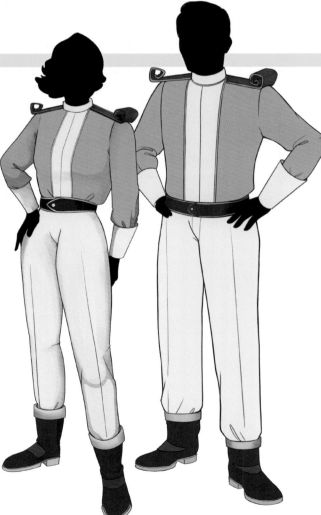

COMMANDER

Worn by commanders of larger WSP installations, the commander's uniform is a modified version of the support staff uniform with gold piping and large gold shoulder epaulettes that carry on down the back of the shirt. This makes the commander immediately recognisable both on the field and in diplomatic situations.

MOBILITY

While operating in space and on the surface of alien worlds, WSP crews have been equipped with mobility aids to assist them when negotiating dangerous terrains.

JETMOBILE

The Jetmobile is a specially designed hoverbike for use when exploring alien worlds and travelling around Space City. A small jet engine is mounted on an antigrav platform that allows the vehicle to effortlessly travel through the air at a top speed of roughly 40 kilometres per hour. An aft compartment allows additional equipment to be stored on board while an integrated raygun and communications array provides the driver with everything needed while in the field.

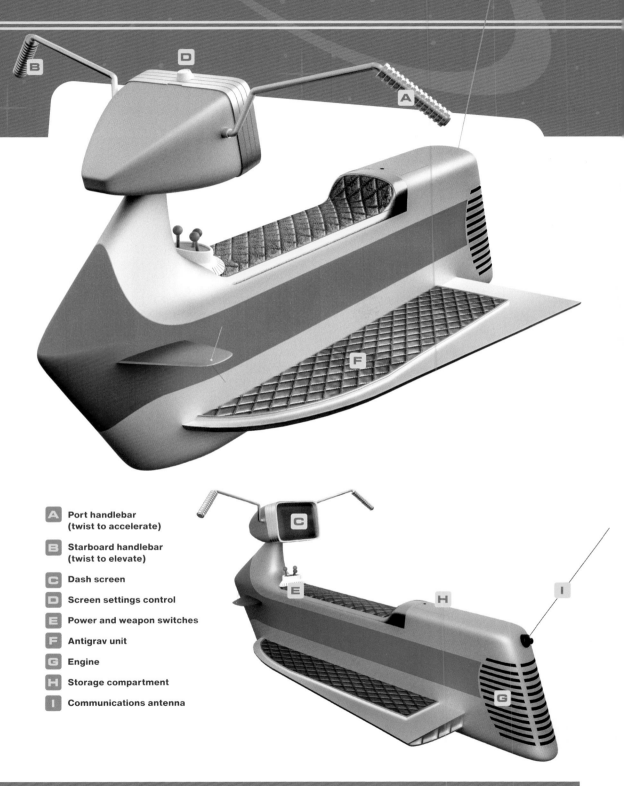

VERSATILITY

An XL-class vessel will most commonly carry one of these vehicles for every crew member, colour coded accordingly. In emergency situations, a Jetmobile can be used to carry an extra person or even pull cargo, but this greatly affects the performance of the vehicle.

LIMITATIONS

While a versatile vehicle with a proven track record in the field, the Jetmobile does have its limitations. Its jet engine requires at least a minimal amount of atmosphere to function and the antigravity system can overheat in dangerously hot environments.

A Port handlebar (twist to accelerate)

B Starboard handlebar (twist to elevate)

C Dash screen

D Screen settings control

E Power and weapon switches

F Antigrav unit

G Engine

H Storage compartment

I Communications antenna

THRUSTER PACK

The compact and easy-to-use nature of the thruster pack has led to it becoming the most common way of transferring between vessels when in space. Given the hazardous nature of the environment, extensive training is given to all cadets to ensure the chances of accidents are minimised as much as possible.

OXYGEN PILLS

While XL-class vessels do carry traditional environment suits for extreme conditions, the development of the oxygen pill has completely eliminated the need for them in a vacuum. Oxygen pills slowly release oxygen into the blood system while an environment field, protected by spacecraft and equipment, stabilises both temperature and pressure to a level that allows safe travel.

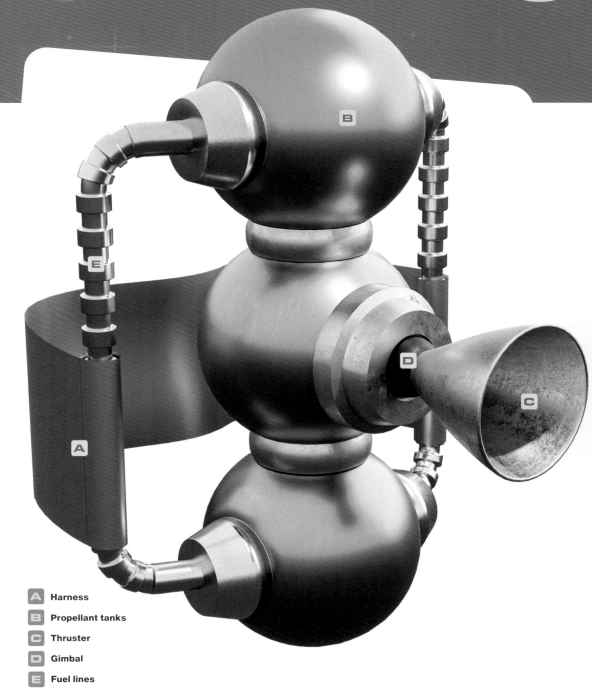

A Harness
B Propellant tanks
C Thruster
D Gimbal
E Fuel lines

STANDARD ISSUE SIDEARM

Currently, the raygun is the primary form of self-defence equipment used across the WSP.

These weapons use gas cartridges and atomic capsules to discharge an energy beam that can either subdue or obliterate its target. The weapons are frequently updated and at the time of writing the organisation is in the process of transitioning from the Mark V raygun to the Mark VI raygun.

POWER SOURCE

The primary energy source for the raygun comes in atomic capsules that are loaded into the base of the weapon. These capsules are extremely volatile when exposed to the open air and will explode after a few minutes if not sealed correctly. One atomic capsule can power the raygun for up to 70 shots at its highest setting.

MARK V RAYGUN

The Mark V iteration of the raygun was first issued in 2055 and widely distributed across the organisation replacing the smaller and less powerful Mark IV. The breakthrough of the Mark V was the ability to adjust the strength of the atomic beam from "destructive" to the harmless but still able to subdue "coma ray". The Mark V was ultimately retired in favour of the sleeker and more compact Mark VI.

- **A** Grip
- **B** Settings dial
- **C** Emitter
- **D** Overheat warning light
- **E** Tactical light

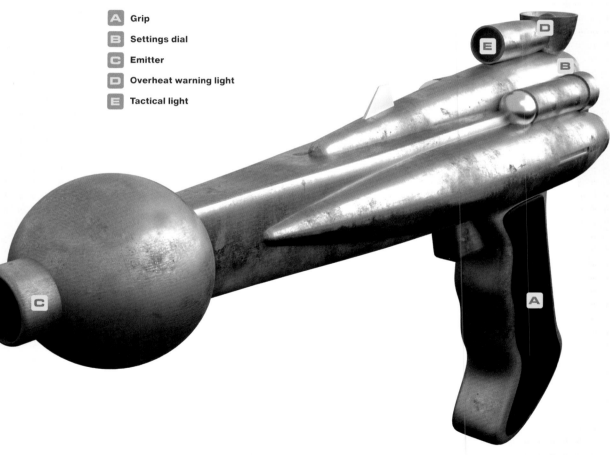

4

RAY BEAM

When firing on coma ray, the weapon discharges a bright flame with a wide area of effect. While short exposure is harmless and renders the target unconscious, prolonged exposure can dangerously irradiate people and objects. A higher, more destructive setting fires a condensed beam which can effortlessly cut through rock and metal.

OLDER MODELS

The newest equipment in the fleet is generally deployed to the frontline outposts and on board the Fireball fleet, where it is needed most. It is not uncommon to see older iterations of field equipment in use around Space City. The armaments available in the Control Tower are still the Mark IV rayguns.

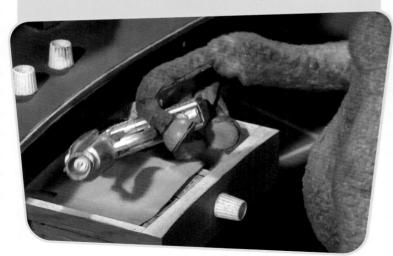

MARK VI RAYGUN

The Mark VI significantly improves on the previous model by miniaturising a lot of the weapon's components and providing a more streamlined shape that sits comfortably in its holster. Improvements in radiator technology have also prevented the weapon from overheating as much as its predecessor.

- **A** Grip
- **B** Settings dial
- **C** Emitter

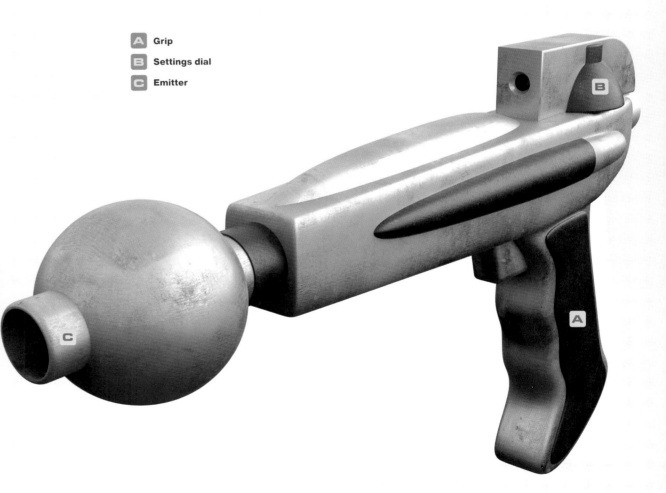

ROBERT THE ROBOT

Robert is the creation of Professor Matic, designed and built in his quest to create the perfect mechanical robot. After years of research, development and fine-tuning, Robert was activated for the first time on July 10th, 2058.

Initially programmed to assist with Professor Matic's experiments, Robert has undergone several upgrades to his robotic brain allowing him to perform increasingly complex tasks. Notable among his regular operating parameters is the ability to co-pilot Fireball XL5 and to control the main body of the ship when Fireball Junior is detached.

Robert communicates using a simulated electronic voice: he often repeats commands to ensure that his instructions have been correctly understood. Robert also boasts enhanced strength and durability. His transparent aluminium body is able to lift loads far greater than any single human and he also has increased resistance to certain types of radiation.

Naturally, Robert does not breathe and can therefore operate in the vacuum of space just as efficiently as in normal atmospheric conditions.

One of Robert's many functions is that he can play the drums, and he has provided backup percussion to the Fireball team during several musical performances.

While the rest of the Fireball XL5 crew need plenty of sleep during patrol missions, Robert can go several months between routine maintenance checks, although Professor Matic prefers to carry these out more regularly to keep Robert in peak condition.

OVERLOAD

Despite his advanced nature, Robert is not infallible. Repeated or conflicting instructions can cause him to overload and "blow his top", sending jets of steam into the air. He is also susceptible to the hypnotic influence of gamma rays, just as his human colleagues are.

In the early days of his operation, Robert's control frequencies could be interrupted by microwave jammers. Professor Matic has since made improvements to Robert's circuitry to prevent him from being taken advantage of in this manner.

A	Main antenna
B	Processor
C	Ocular sensors
D	Speakers
E	Proximity sensors

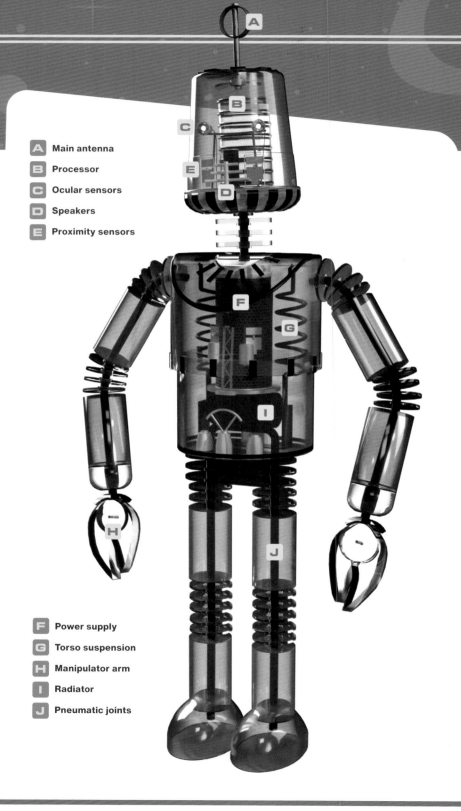

F	Power supply
G	Torso suspension
H	Manipulator arm
I	Radiator
J	Pneumatic joints

ANTENNA

Recently, Professor Matic noticed a mysterious upgrade to Robert's antenna. With no memory of making the modification, this implies that either someone else has been modifying Robert or that Robert has been modifying himself, the ramifications of which could point to Robert slowly becoming sentient. It is also possible that the Professor just forgot – most likely the answer!

Section 5
KEY PERSONNEL

FIREBALL XL5 CREW AND SPACE CITY KEY PERSONNEL

There are countless vocations available to the personnel assigned to Space City from control room technicians to medical staff, broadcasting engineers to transport controllers – almost every kind of occupation can be found within the confines of the spaceport. But there is one job that is the envy of many Space City pilots and astronauts: a posting to the crew of an XL-class cruiser.

These illustrious assignments, however, are not earned easily and only those personnel who consistently meet or exceed the highest standards of excellence in their duties can hope to be considered.

Years of academic study, complex test flights, gruelling solo patrols, and tough physical and mental training are just some of the hurdles that lie in wait for anyone contemplating the role.

These rigorous criteria are especially paramount for the crew of Fireball XL5. As the personnel responsible for the operation of the WSP's flagship craft, the crew of XL5 work incredibly hard to prove themselves as the best examples of humanity whether on routine patrol missions or as diplomatic representatives of Earth. They are all remarkable as individuals, but as a crew they are exemplars in the finest tradition of the WSP.

The following personnel files detail the background of Fireball XL5's crew: Colonel Steve Zodiac, Doctor Venus and Professor Matthew Matic, as well as providing information on Commander Wilbur Zero and Lieutenant Josef Ninety – two of Space City's key personnel.

Born: October 29th, 2030 – Kahra, Mars

Occupation: Astronaut

Current Assignment:
Commanding Officer and Pilot – Fireball XL5

COLONEL STEVE ZODIAC

Steve Zodiac was born on Mars in the domed city of Kahra in the year 2030. His family moved to the red planet from the United States of America so that Steve's father, a distinguished air marshal, could become the head of the Universal Secret Service. Life on another planet had a profound effect on the young boy, and as a result, Steve developed a keen interest in the possibility of life beyond the solar system.

When he was 17-years-old, Steve enrolled in the World Space Patrol Academy as one of its first students. By 2051, he had attained his astronaut's licence and was posted to Space City as a sub-lieutenant. During his early days at Space City, Steve formed a firm friendship with Major Jim Ireland who would go on to become one of the most famous names in the field of space exploration.

After a few short years, Steve gained a promotion to the rank of lieutenant and was soon flying shuttle services between Earth and the other human colonies in the vicinity of the solar system. The experience gained proved invaluable when he was promoted to captain and assigned to duty with the new XL patrol fleet in 2055. Under the watchful eye of Colonel Grange, Steve became co-pilot of Fireball XL5, and gained a reputation for nerves of steel while flying patrol missions over the next two years.

2057, however, would prove to be a major turning point in the young captain's career. During a test flight to assess a newly installed nutomic motor, Colonel Grange suffered a nervous breakdown at the controls and Steve was forced to knock him out. Steve reported the situation to Space City and continued with the test flight, averting any further incident.

His quick-thinking and cool head did not go unnoticed and as a direct result of his action, Steve was promoted to the rank of colonel and given command of Fireball XL5 along with a crew of his choice. Without hesitation, Steve selected Doctor Venus and Professor Matthew Matic to accompany him on patrol duty of Sector 25, a routine patrol that continues to this day.

Commander Zero has noted that Steve is the best space pilot in the service and in 2063 Steve was awarded the honour of Astronaut of the Year.

Although XL5's missions can often be hazardous bringing the crew into contact with hostile races, Steve's preferred solution is to resolve matters without resorting to the use of force whenever possible.

In his off-duty moments, Steve enjoys keeping a personal log of his exploits, watching interplanetary ball games on television and entertaining guests at his executive apartment – the envy of the other pilots at Space City.

Born: February 10th, 2035 – Paris, France

Occupation: Doctor of Space Medicine

Current Assignment:
Medical Officer – Fireball XL5

DOCTOR VENUS

Venus was born Lily Lumière during a particularly turbulent period of history. In the wake of the Atomic War of 2028, the mass rioting in France claimed the lives of both of her parents but by a miracle Lily escaped their fate and was found concealed in a survival shelter by an emergency medical team. She was placed in a state orphanage and eventually adopted by Doctor Victor Crabtree, a physician sent to help in the aftermath of the war.

It was Victor who gave his adopted daughter the name Venus, and together with his wife, the trio made a new home in the south of France in 2040. Victor never hid the truth of Venus's origin from her and, when she was old enough to understand, he told her exactly what had happened. Venus was grateful, and although she loved her adopted parents dearly, she expressed a desire to discover who her blood family really was.

After much patient searching, the family discovered a distant relative in Paris who was able to verify that Venus was actually Lily. Although pleased to have solved the mystery of her birth identity, Venus elected to continue using the name that her adopted parents had given her. She was later encouraged to study medicine – a course of action that led her to graduate from Universe University with a PhD in Biology and Space Medicine.

Venus's compassionate nature and unwavering desire to help others in need resulted in her joining the WSP medical programme in 2056. A posting to Space City had Venus overseeing the stresses and pressures involved in the operation of the new XL ships and one of her key responsibilities was to ensure the crews were not under more strain than their bodies could handle.

In 2057, Venus was promoted to surgeon lieutenant and reassigned from the Space City Medical Wing to Fireball XL5 under Steve Zodiac's command. The pair quickly became close friends, despite Steve's personal apprehension about daily medical checks.

On a mission to the planet Calevio in May 2062, Venus adopted a wounded Lazoon, named him Zoonie and nursed him back to health. The following year Venus completed further medical studies and earned a Diploma in Space Psychology.

In addition to her formidable skills in the field of space medicine, Venus is also a capable co-pilot and often assists with navigation duties. Her exceptional skills and continued dedication to duty have resulted in several offers to transfer to other vessels, but Venus has loyally elected to remain with Fireball XL5.

When not on an active patrol assignment or conducting private research, Venus enjoys listening to the latest music discs in her comfortable beach house located a few kilometres along the coast from Space City's control tower.

5

PROFESSOR MATTHEW MATIC

Born: October 5th, 2012 – London, Great Britain

Occupation: Science Officer

**Current Assignment:
Navigator and Science Specialist – Fireball XL5**

Matthew Matic only spent a few short years in the country of his birth before his family relocated to Houston, Texas, United States of America where he spent the remainder of his childhood years.

Matthew's father was a project leader at the former Glenn Field experimental space launch facility and the young Matt would often be allowed to view rocket launches. These events only served to further Matt's growing fascination with science and space exploration.

Enrolling at Universe University, Matt gained a reputation for his ability to solve the most complex problems using brilliant, if unorthodox, solutions. It was during this time that he met Doctor Bernard Stamp and Doctor Howard Rootes, who he would re-encounter years later during his service with the WSP.

In 2033, Matt graduated with a then unheard of 21 degrees in astrophysics, robotics and astronomy. His stellar reputation preceded him and it wasn't long before he was headhunted for the prestigious position of navigator on the recently constructed XK series of interplanetary rockets.

His first space mission as navigator on board XK1 introduced him to co-pilot Wilbur Zero, who would eventually go on to become Commander of Space City. Matt's navigation duties with the XK series continued for several years until, in 2045, he accepted a professorship at his alma mater, Universe University. He lectured on the field of hyperdrive technology and astronomy, and widely became known by students as "the thinking man's professor".

By 2050, Matt had designed and built the world's first nutomic hyperdrive motor which proved to be a major step forward for the future of space exploration. The XK ships, while revolutionary in their day, were not equipped for rapid travel between planets and Matt's new motor design would cut the transit time from months to just days in some cases. The implications of the remarkable design were not lost on the top brass and Matt was offered the position of Research and Development Head on the upcoming XL project. The posting included the honorary rank of major, something that Matt accepted with his trademark humility.

Matt's nutomic engines entered active service in 2051. After trial runs on the Century 21 prototype (later known as Fireball XL0), the engine was fitted to Fireball XL1-Alpha. By 2057, all the Fireball XL ships had been outfitted with this new technology. Faced with the real prospect of exploring alien worlds, Matt requested a posting on one of the new ships. To the delight of Steve Zodiac, the professor accepted a request to join the crew of Fireball XL5 and Matt has stuck with Steve and the rest of the crew through thick and thin ever since.

Matt is never one to waste his off-duty time and enjoys indulging in a wide variety of passions including fishing, amatuer magic tricks and tinkering with his robotic creation, Robert.

Born: Uncertain, estimated 2055 – planet Calevio

Occupation: Lazoon

Current Assignment:
Venus's pet and honorary member of crew – Fireball XL5

ZOONIE THE LAZOON

Zoonie is a lazoon, originally native to the planet Calevio. During a mission to that world, the crew of Fireball XL5 found him gravely injured. Venus took it upon herself to treat Zoonie's wounds and nurse him back to health. By the time Fireball Junior was ready to return to orbit, Zoonie refused to part company with his rescuers and, with the crew in agreement, Venus adopted Zoonie as a pet.

His apparent lazy demeanour is a common trait of his species and it is often difficult to motivate him to do anything other than sleep! However, after months of patience, Venus was eventually able to teach him a small selection of human phrases including; "welcome home", "howdy folks" and "follow me".

Like other lazoons and many of the creatures native to Calevio, Zoonie has demonstrated empathic abilities. In the past he has been able to detect electromagnetic disturbances and sense strong emotions in other living beings.

While most humans tend to find Zoonie's appearance to be rather cute, the same cannot be said for everyone. Lillispatians are terrified by lazoons, a fact that the XL5 crew exploited when the Lillispatians attempted to turn several humans into their slaves.

The Zanadus of planet Zanadu consider the lazoon species to be their mortal enemies. Kudos, the last of the Zanadus, even formulated a plan to kill Zoonie, but thankfully the attempt was thwarted before it could succeed.

Zoonie has an evident fondness for Martian Delight, which he is allowed to eat if he has been good. Another of his favourite foods is haggis, something which Jock Campbell was delighted to discover.

Although Zoonie is fond of jazz music, he dislikes loud noises and has no time for television, which sends him to sleep.

On the occasions when he is fully awake, Zoonie's natural curiosity and a knack for getting into trouble often causes chaos for the crew of Fireball XL5 and the personnel of Space City. However, the lazoon has a heart of gold and it's no exaggeration to say that his actions have proved invaluable in saving lives on more than one occasion.

Born: **June 27th, 2017 – New York City, United States of America**

Occupation: **Command Division Officer**

Current Assignment: **Controller of Operations – Space City**

COMMANDER JONATHAN WILBUR ZERO

Jonathan Wilbur Zero, known to his friends as Wilbur, grew up in an incredibly strict military family and had the virtues of honour, duty and hard work impressed upon him from a very young age. It was always expected that he would follow in the footsteps of his father and older brothers and enlist in the army. However, in an act of what his family considered to be rebellion, Jonathan enlisted in the United States Air Force in 2036.

He quickly became one of the most talented pilots in his unit and in 2040, when the XK programme at Glenn Field were searching for the best fliers for their new rockets, Jonathan was chosen and awarded the rank of lieutenant.

For five years he acted as co-pilot on several XK rockets, often alongside Matthew Matic. When Matt left the XK programme in 2045, Jonathan was promoted to captain and given command of XK2. Two years later, Jonathan single-handedly saved Glenn Field from destruction when he flew a daredevil mission to destroy a faulty meteor demolition missile. He was quickly promoted to colonel for his selfless act of bravery, but to this day prefers not to talk about the incident.

By 2048, Jonathan was well established as a pioneer of space travel and took up a transfer to the newly founded WSP headquarters in Space City as chief astronaut. He performed the function of vice commander under General Rossiter.

In 2052, Rossiter moved on to take a seat at the World Security Council, leaving Jonathan to be promoted to commander in the wake of his absence. He also married his long-time love, Eleanor, during that same year and their son, also called Jonathan, was born not one year later.

Nowadays, Jonathan still remains in command of Space City, albeit with the young and eager Lieutenant Ninety around to help. Whether sat behind his neutroni transmitting console, or flying through the reaches of space, Jonathan is a vital part of the WSP organisation.

His gruff and efficient style of command has earned him the nickname "the Terror of Space City", a moniker that he is well aware of. However, those who know him well know that under the gruff exterior, Jonathan has a kind heart and a sense of humour.

One of his greatest regrets is that he once lost a chance at promotion because of his involvement in the Skyball 1 fiasco, but he has since come to terms with the incident and looks upon it with a reflectiveness born of experience.

While often confined to the operations room in Space City's control tower, Jonathan is also the astronaut in charge of Space Rescue 1 when it is required, a role that he takes every bit as seriously as his regular duties.

Born: January 7th, 2039 – Katannia, Bereznik

Occupation: Command Division Officer

Current Assignment:
Deputy Controller of Operations – Space City

LIEUTENANT JOSEF NINETY

Josef Nineski was born into the cruel clutches of the Bereznik police state, a nation built upon the remains of Poland in the aftermath of the European Atomic War of 2028. His family held no sympathy with the dictatorship and were able to escape to the west in 2045.

Upon arrival, the family name was changed from Nineski to 'Ninety' so they could integrate better with the western world. Not much is known about the tutelage Josef received in Bereznik or the west, but he was skilled enough in electronics to qualify for a working position at the WSP in 2060 as neutroni communications officer and one of the data management personnel. He received promotion to lieutenant and became the Space City subcontroller to Commander Zero in 2062.

Later that same year, Josef underwent training to become a full-time astronaut, which he passed by the skin of his teeth after his space capsule nearly exploded with him inside. At present, he is still the subcontroller at Space City, but his astronaut's wings have given him the opportunity to act as co-pilot alongside Commander Zero on rescue missions. He is also undertaking a practical design degree course in electronics, which he hopes to pass and become a Bachelor of Space, with an added promotion to full controller.

Josef resides in apartment 30269, one of many of the residences for the lower ranking officers in the accommodation block a few kilometres from Space City. He maintains a close friendship with the crew of Fireball XL5, and often spends time with them when they are off duty.

Steve Zodiac was one of the first to pick up on Josef's desire to become an astronaut and took it upon himself to help the lieutenant earn his astronaut's wings. As a result, Josef has spent countless hours as the co-pilot of Fireball XL5 on training flights and has developed a working knowledge of the XL ships that makes him the envy of other junior officers at Space City.

Like Venus, Josef enjoys listening to music and he is also an accomplished musician himself. During a television special filmed at Space City, Josef gave a performance on the double bass as part of a musical number which earned him a standing ovation.

JOCK CAMPBELL

Born: September 6th, 2018 – Edinburgh, Great Britain

Occupation: Engineer

Current Assignment:
Chief of Engineering Operations – Space City

Jock Campbell was born in Edinburgh and from a young age he was fascinated with anything mechanical. He would later attribute this sense of wonder to a toy construction set that he received one Christmas from his parents.

Unlike many of Space City's illustrious personnel, Jock didn't spend his formative years looking to the stars. Instead, he spent his education studying Earth-based engineering, design and energy management. He particularly relished solving problems arising during the development of new building projects.

It wasn't until 2040, when Jock had a chance encounter with the chairman of Barrett Aerospace Overseas Corporation (BAOC), that his future career path would begin to take shape. The meeting impressed the chairman to such a degree that Jock was appointed as project leader for the BAOC terminal expansion at London Airport.

Eight years and numerous successful projects later, Jock was assigned to Space City in the early stages of its construction. He brought the same hard-working ethic and dedication to the job as he had shown on previous developments and was instrumental in planning the rotation mechanism for the main control tower.

By the time construction on Space City was completed, Jock had risen to the position of chief engineer with hundreds of equally hard-working men and women reporting to him. Jock considers the often high-pressure nature of his work to be the perfect tonic, and he is never happier than when he's solving a new engineering problem.

Although Space City is far from his childhood home, Jock has never lost his Scottish identity. He will happily play the bagpipes for anyone who asks and is only too glad to share a haggis with his colleagues.

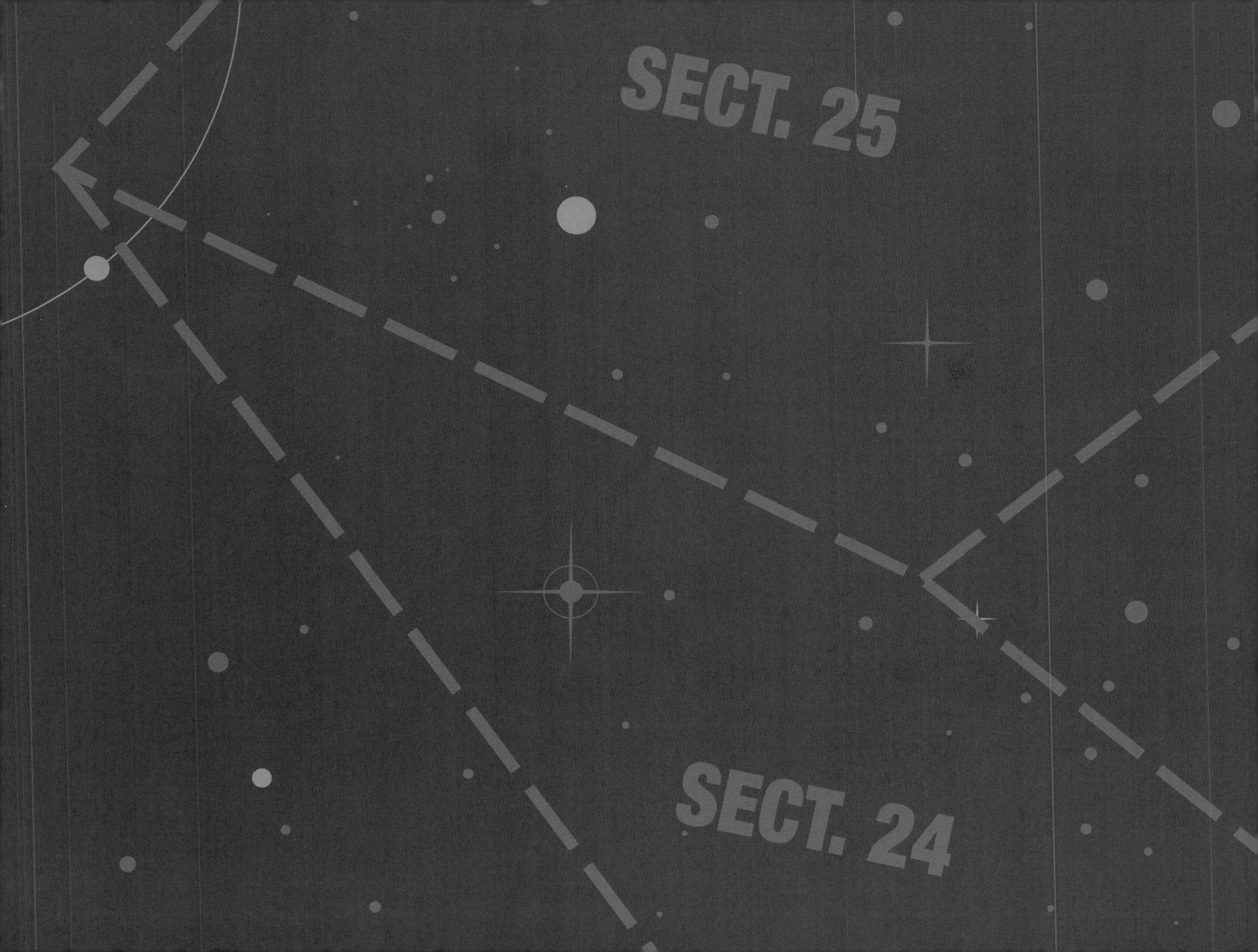
SECT. 25
SECT. 24

Section 6

GALACTIC OVERVIEW

6

INTRODUCTION

At time of writing, the WSP's sphere of influence encompasses 30 sectors. These sectors don't necessarily comprise Earth's space but an area that the WSP is allowed to operate in through treaties of exploration, civilisations that have an agreement with the WSP to protect them or unclaimed territory which is still patrolled to monitor for upcoming threats.

While the WSP has made many allies and generally has good standing on the galactic stage as a fair and balanced force striving for universal peace, it does have enemies that either wish to see its destruction or to capture Earth itself.

This section will outline several of the races that have posed or continue to pose a threat to humanity that you may encounter in the future.

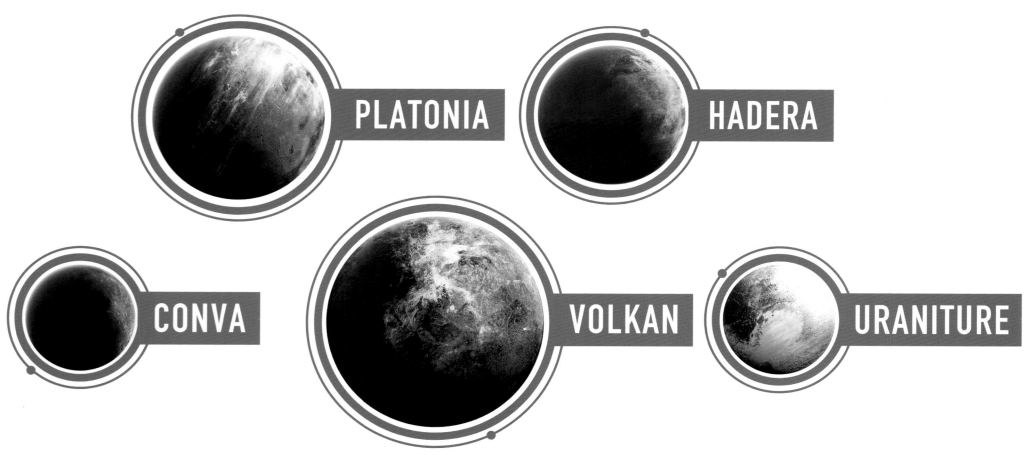

PLATONIA

HADERA

CONVA

VOLKAN

URANITURE

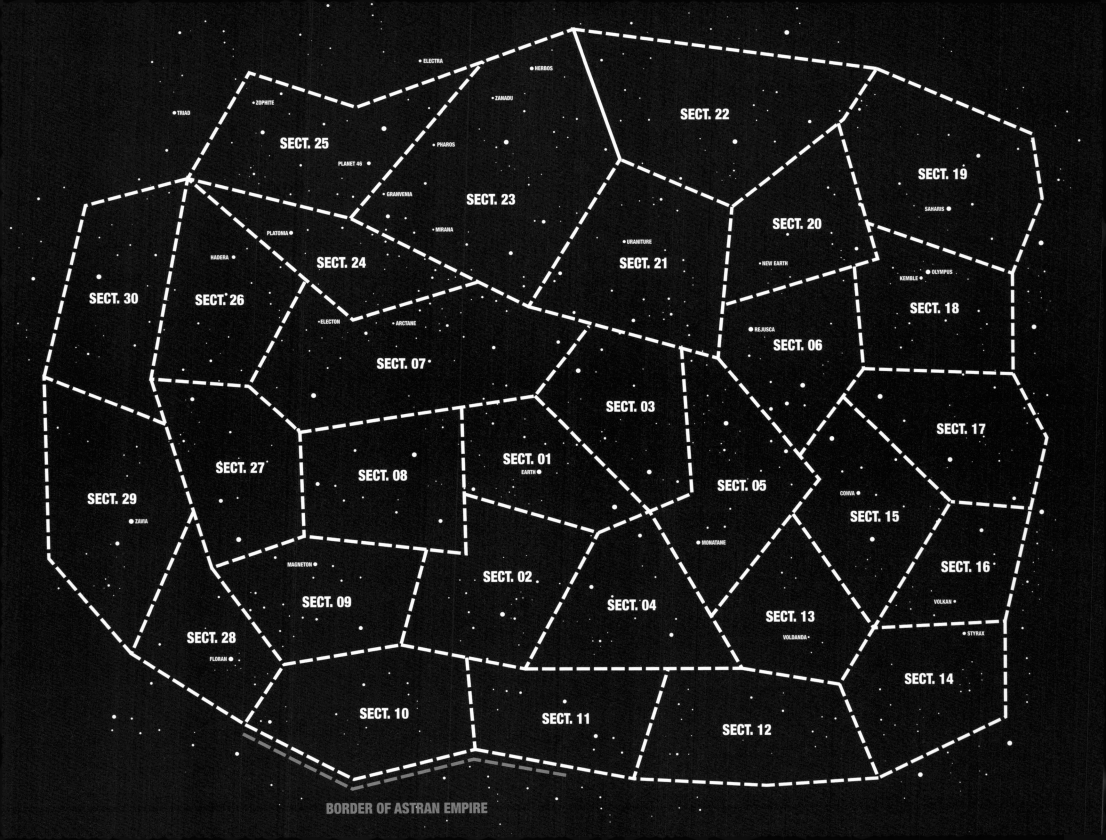

BORDER OF ASTRAN EMPIRE

THE SUBTERRAINS

P lanet 46 is an obscure planetoid located in Sector 25. Only once visited before by a survey craft back in 2050, the planet was deemed "geologically unremarkable with limited flora", though it was noted that the crew felt a general sense of unease while exploring the surface observing many rock features taking on the shape of vicious monsters. While the idea was posited that these may indicate evidence of a long-dead civilisation, they were eventually chalked up to natural occurrences and Planet 46 was forgotten with no plans for further inspection. Little did the survey team know that their presence had been noticed and their invasion would not be forgiven.

Thirteen years later, a planetomic missile was intercepted on a direct course for Earth – its origin, Planet 46. Fireball XL5 was dispatched to investigate and its crew discovered the secret of Planet 46 – an entire civilisation of Subterrains living beneath the planet's surface intent on the destruction of Earth. The crew of XL5 were able to escape Planet 46, capturing the leader of the Subterrains and narrowly thwarting another attack on Earth.

APPEARANCE

The Subterrains are humanoid but their skin has an almost insectoid appearance. It has been noted that the Subterrain base is well lit and their eyes are perfectly adapted to seeing on the surface indicating they may have been driven underground at some point in the past by an invader or natural disaster. In terms of strength and performance, the Subterrains are comparable to humans. They are very intelligent and creative, being able to convert the limited resources of their planet into advanced technology.

SPACECRAFT

The Subterrains operate a small fleet of spacecraft that use a configuration similar to vessels used by the Platonians. It has been theorised that the Subterrains have been spying on other cultures and reverse engineering their technology.

ONGOING OBSERVATION

The Subterrains represent a moral crisis for the WSP as their planet is deep within Earth's space borders and their aggressive expansion has accidentally threatened the sovereignty of the Subterrains. They have completely ignored all calls for a diplomatic resolution and their leader has refused to cooperate or reveal further information about his race. With their xenophobic nature and continued attacks on Earth and WSP personnel, an exclusion zone has been set up around Planet 46's solar system and the decision made to keep them under observation for the time being.

THE ASTRAN EMPIRE

It's easy to forget that despite how far humankind has come in its journey into space, they are still a relatively new player on the galactic stage – and not all will welcome such a rapidly expanding power arriving on their borders.

Early in the human expansion era, a lone expedition craft was destroyed when exploring the edges of what we now refer to as Sector 12. A TA craft that was dispatched to investigate almost met with the same fate, but managed to limp home with the first images of what would become humankind's strongest competitor, the Astrans. Word was soon passed to the humans via diplomatic channels: this is Astran space, and you are not welcome.

Since then, Earth's diplomats have been attempting to secure dialogue with the Astran Empire and, after a long drawn-out negotiation, Earth welcomed the first ambassador from Astra whose main role was to determine where a hard border between the two powers should lie. This fragile peace was almost entirely derailed when an Earth fleet on manoeuvres strayed too close to an Astran fleet that had been instructed to observe them and all-out conflict ensued. A cease-fire was reached and in an effort to de-escalate from a galactic war the Astran chief, the Kaplan – equivalent to the World President – made a diplomatic visit to Earth. But this too ended in disaster when a human assassin murdered the Kaplan in the middle of a crowded parade.

Conflict seemed inevitable but through a combined effort by the crews of Fireball XL5, Stingray and two unknown secret service agents, it was uncovered that the entire war had been orchestrated by the Kaplan Minus, the second in command of the Astran Empire, in a bid to seize power and crush Astra's biggest rival. Ironically, the cooperation between the human and Astran forces in uncovering this threat forged a path to the beginning of a new era of peace between the two powers.

At the time of writing, peace talks between Astra and Earth are still ongoing, but it is believed that agreements for sharing scientific knowledge and trade will be made within the next few years.

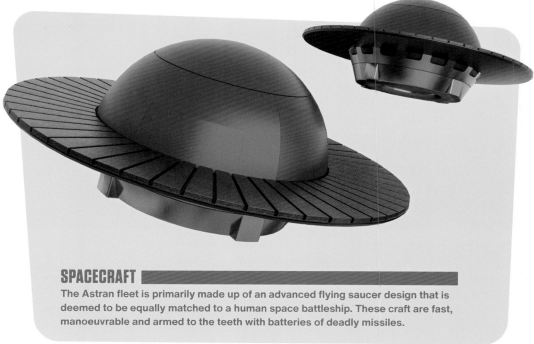

SPACECRAFT

The Astran fleet is primarily made up of an advanced flying saucer design that is deemed to be equally matched to a human space battleship. These craft are fast, manoeuvrable and armed to the teeth with batteries of deadly missiles.

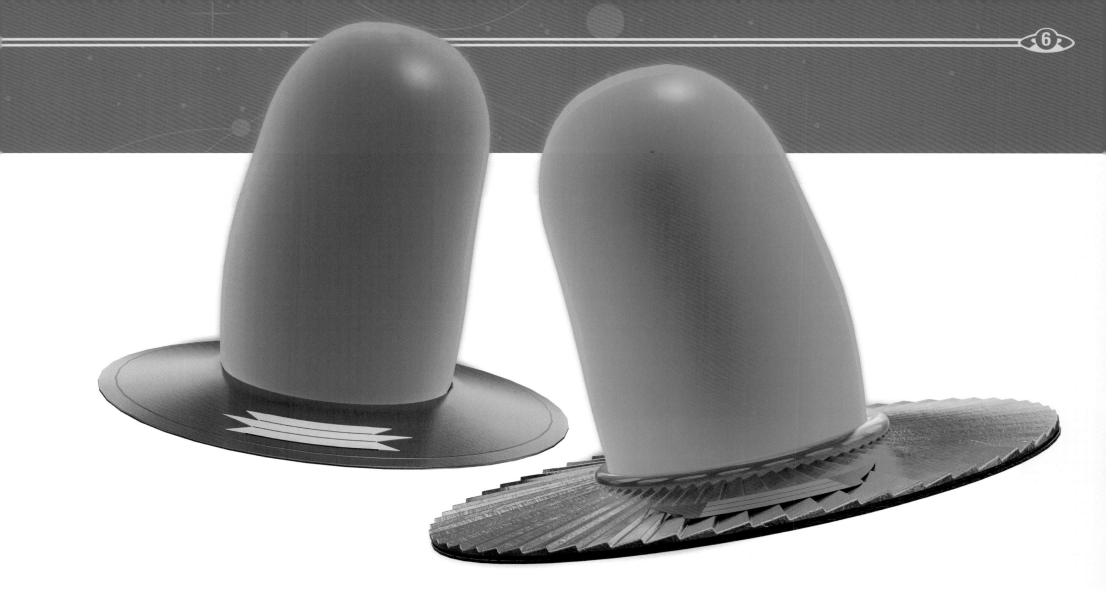

BIOLOGY

The Astrans are undoubtedly the most alien of the various species humankind has discovered, which may have greatly contributed to the mutual mistrust between the two powers.

At first glance, an Astran resembles a glowing rubbery capsule-like shape that is only capable of limited movement without their hover discs – antigravity rings that they use to travel around on. It is believed that the outer layer is actually a protective shell and the real Astran, a gelatinous creature, lives inside. It is theorised that the Astrans evolved in the swamp regions of Astra and they require this protective coating to survive outside their native habitat.

The Astrans have no visible arms or legs but they have telekinetic powers which they use for basic movement and manipulating objects. They can also use these powers to cause harm – filtering lenses on their hover discs convert their telekinetic powers into a deadly laser. The Astrans have been seen in a range of colours but these don't seem to be tied into any specific rank structure.

THE AQUAPHIBIANS

The less we know about something the more fear it evokes and this is certainly true of what could possibly be one of the newest and greatest threats to the galactic community. In mid-2063, Fireball XL5 responded to an "Emergency Red" distress call from the planet Zophite declaring that an aggressive alien species was attacking their planet – with only two survivors holding out in a concealed underground bunker.

When Fireball XL5 arrived, one of the hostile creatures remained and it was able to cripple Fireball Junior with a powerful laser beam and poisonous gas cloud. Barely escaping, Fireball XL5 remained in orbit while Professor Matic came up with a defence against the creature's ray attack. With the hull of Fireball Junior now coated in a chemical able to withstand and refract the alien's weapon, Colonel Zodiac and Doctor Venus were able to return to the planet and temporarily ward off the creature with a missile, then dive beneath the ocean surface with the alien in hot pursuit.

Arriving at the underground bunker, they made contact with the survivors but the Aquaphibian had followed them to the sanctuary and tried to force them out using its poisonous gas weapon. Colonel Zodiac was able to score a direct hit on the creature with a missile from his hoverbike stunning it and allowing everyone to make a hasty escape.

ZOPHITE CITY

A remote survey probe was dispatched to Zophite to conduct a reconnaissance of the planet and determine the status of the Aquaphibians but it came back negative. The colony was now a ruin with no sign of the creatures. They had simply appeared, wiped out the Zophite civilisation and retreated with no clear motive. By examining this attack, the WSP were able to retrospectively attribute other mysterious events to them as well.

WEAPON

The Aquaphibian that attacked Fireball XL5 wielded an unusual double-barrelled weapon with the top barrel emitting a high-powered laser beam, and the secondary barrel firing a poisonous gas that could also be ignited to cause widespread destruction.

BIOLOGY

Our current understanding of the Aquaphibian is limited. Their name, originated by the Zophites, is a descriptive term reflecting their water-based nature. From footage captured by the crew of Fireball XL5 and through analysing their behaviour, we have been able to draw several conclusions. The Aquaphibians are 2–2.5 metres tall and possess high levels of strength. They have a scaly outer skin which is resistant to coma ray and light missile attacks. They are able to function equally well underwater as on land, and are extremely aggressive. Their level of technology implies an advanced civilization but there are no reports of communication between them. Their origin, species name and motivations are all unknown.

THE INVADERS

Known simply as the Invaders – a direct translation of the name of their people from their native language – this mysterious species has come closer than any other of the WSP's enemies to seizing control of Earth.

Arriving under the cover of a large gaseous cloud that was designated by Space City as a rogue space phenomenon, the Invaders were able to throw Earth's neutroni communications network into disarray and destroy Fireballs XL18 and XL24 who had been dispatched to disperse the cloud. As the cloud enveloped Earth, defences and weapons across the planet became inoperable, and it was only then that the realisation of what was happening dawned on humanity. This was an invasion.

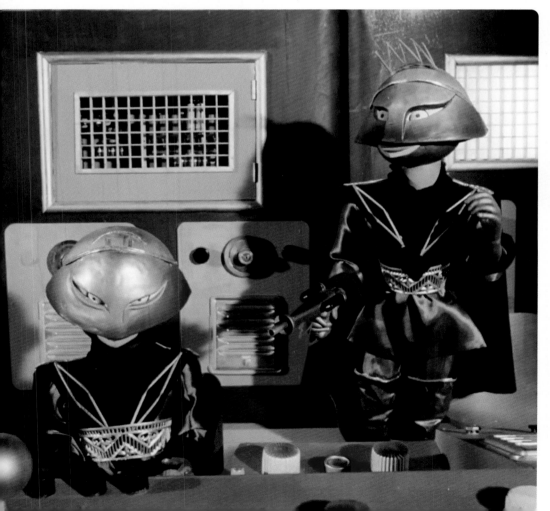

After a paralysing few hours of waiting, large spacecraft eventually descended from the cloud across Space City seeking a beachhead from which to coordinate their land invasion. With no weapons, Space City was quickly overrun and the Invaders' commander and his lieutenant took over the Space City operations room, holding Commander Zero hostage and using threats of violence against his son to ensure cooperation.

With Fireball XL5 stationed in orbit having just returned from inoculating outposts from a galaxy-wide epidemic of Restamesia, the Invaders' commander ordered Commander Zero to give them clearance for landing before activating Space City's interceptor system with the intention of destroying XL5 on its approach. Just when he was about to give the order to fire, however, the Invaders' commander collapsed, along with his lieutenant and every other Invader inside the base. It transpired that as they had travelled from outside the local galactic community they had no resistance to Restamesia, and without being vaccinated succumbed to it almost immediately on exposure.

SHIPS

The Invaders' fleet of spacecraft was taken completely intact by the WSP and offered many insights into their technology. Their ships are designed for stealth but have enough weapons on board to go toe to toe with an XL-class patrol ship. They operate using a crew of five with a cargo bay that can be employed to carry supplies or transport troops. Landing on long legs to keep the vessel safe from ground attack, the entire cargo section is lowered to ground level to allow its complement of soldiers to disembark all at once.

Given the sheer number of Invaders now captive on Earth, the decision was made to transport them to an uninhabited but colonisable world where they could live in comfort, and more could be learned about them and their origins.

While ultimately the Invaders' plans were foiled, it was very apparent that this was due to a fluke of nature and that Earth's forces were completely unprepared for such an attack. This event directly led to the introduction of Earth's defence fleets and the Space Battleships.

BIOLOGY

The Invaders are closely comparable to humans in many ways with a key difference being an exoskeletal skull and carapace making them very resilient to the elements, and their skin appears in differing shades of black and gold. They are very intelligent with key skills of manipulating and weaponising gas, and long-distance intelligence gathering.

Their language is extremely complicated and difficult to translate via the WSP's computers. This, coupled with their xenophobic tendencies, has meant that cooperation between humans and the captive Invaders has been extremely difficult.

G THE GRANATOIDS

In the early expansion era of the 2020s, humankind spread across the stars unopposed, setting up colonies, scientific bases and trading hubs across the frontier. This expansion into the unknown regions of space could have been viewed as reckless and human overconfidence would soon be checked.

When a fledgling colony on Planet 22 went silent, a reconnaissance mission of a TA craft commanded by Colonel Jack Doughty was launched immediately to establish the cause. What he found was nothing more than the charred remains of a settlement, crushed under the weight of giant tyres, leaving tracks and huge gouges in the planet's surface where rare mineral deposits once lay.

On the route back from Planet 22, Doughty received a distress signal broadcast from a scientific expedition on Planet 13. They were under attack by an unstoppable robotic army resistant to all forms of available weaponry. In a desperate manoeuvre that earned him the much coveted "Astronaut of the Year" award, Doughty was able to rescue the science team before they were overrun by the opposing force. From this encounter, they were able to gather invaluable intelligence on the enemy including their origin, purpose and name.

The Granatoids are a race of almost identical robots from the planet Granatoid. The exact nature of how they came to be is shrouded in mystery, but it is believed that they must have been created by some sort of intelligence that had either abandoned them or been destroyed by them. They are composed of a currently unknown metal that renders them completely indestructible which, at the time of writing, is unique to Granatoid. It is believed that the resource is now depleted on their home planet and the Granatoids are on a mission to find another source and establish a new base from which to expand their number. While this in itself is not a problem, the Granatoids harbour a disdain for organic life and will go out of their way to eliminate any presence they encounter while scouring worlds for the metal they seek.

Over the next few years, the Granatoids would be a persistent threat to humanity with their appearance on any planet forcing an immediate evacuation and retreat with no way of stopping them. Through a fluke discovery, however, a geological survey ship that was unable to escape from the Granatoid advance was inexplicably spared, and it was realised that the mineral they had been sent to investigate, plyton, had overwhelmed the Granatoid's central processing units forcing them not only to withdraw but leave the planet entirely.

Over the next 50 years, the Granatoids would appear in Earth space and be intercepted by the WSP using a supply of plyton to repel them. This is a temporary solution, however. The supply of plyton is rapidly drying up and soon humankind will once again have nothing to counter the threat of the Granatoids.

MA DOUGHTY

In 2063, Fireball XL5 was dispatched to rescue the crew of a scientific research station on Planet 73 after a platoon of Granatoid tanks landed on the far side of the planet. With no further supplies of plyton, Professor Matic tried to rig up a device to simulate its effects – but to no effect. The entire crew was nearly overrun by Granatoid forces until Ma Doughty, daughter of Colonel Jack Doughty who had stowed away on board XL5, appeared to ward off the tanks merely by her presence. It transpired that a necklace given to her by her father was made of plyton and was enough to disperse the Granatoids.

TANKS

Made from the same material, the Granatoid tanks are easily as iconic as the robots themselves. These rather simple combat vehicles feature a powerful cannon and advanced sensors to accurately map the environment ahead of them. While only distanced observations of these vehicles have been made due to the danger they pose, it is believed that they are designed to travel across the surface of an entire planet, obliterating everything in their path while using the front antenna to scan the surface for metal deposits.

THE ARCONS

L ocated a few light years outside the edge of Sector 25 and beyond Earth space lies the planet Electra. Unlike many of the races listed in this section, much is known about its inhabitants, the Arcons, who have been a persistent thorn in the side of the WSP for many years. While not posing as much of a tangible threat as the Granatoids or the Aquaphibians due to the limited operational range of their vessels, they have still proved to be a major hazard to nearby civilisations and shipping in their ongoing pursuit to accumulate new technology. However, it wasn't until 2064 that it became apparent to the WSP that their initial assessment of the Arcons may have been misjudged.

In mid-2064, Fireball XL5 was returning from a routine patrol in Sector 25 when a bomb in its space gyro detonated, crippling the vessel and stranding it in space. An Arcon ship appeared and used its gamma ray to stun the crew and take them to Arcon. It turned out that over the course of many years, the Arcons had infiltrated the WSP and while in disguise had been planting neutroni bombs across the fleet and in Space City itself, their plan being that once detonated it would draw rescue ships in which they would capture to assemble an armada and overrun Earth space and Earth itself.

However, held in the same room that the Arcons were using to store their gamma ray-resistant eyewear, the Fireball XL5 captives were able to utilise the goggles and escape aboard a Gamma ship. The Arcons' audacious plan had been executed to perfection but ultimately failed due to the Arcons' disdain and disrespect for other cultures causing them to underestimate their captives.

Upon returning to Earth, a large-scale inquiry was conducted in order to root out all Arcon agents masquerading as humans in Space City. The Gamma ship was disassembled and a countermeasure to its paralysing ray was developed, with a blockade established between Arcon and Earth space. At time of writing, the Arcons have continued to ignore any diplomatic overtures with occasional attacks being made on the blockade.

ELECTRA

The surface of Electra is bright yellow in colour due to the high sulphur content in the soil. Large lithium deposits on the planet allow the Arcons ample materials to build power stations and create batteries in order to sustain themselves.

APPEARANCE

The Arcons themselves are grey and yellow skinned bipeds, similar to humans but appearing much more skeletal in nature having evolved to draw energy directly from electricity rather than food and nutrients like other species. Their eyes also glow showing the energy flowing through them, but the lights fade when they are in need of recharging.

They are incredibly arrogant and dismissive of other civilisations which makes them difficult to negotiate with, but they do possess a strong curiosity about the technology of others.

SHIPS

The Gamma ships used by the Arcons are incredibly advanced vessels that utilise an ion drive for propulsion. While smaller than a Fireball, these ships are fast and agile but limited in range due to their power supply coming from onboard batteries that are recharged on Electra. Rather than utilising destructive weaponry, the Arcons favour non-destructive weapons in order to capture vessels intact and steal their technology. This is demonstrated by the large gamma ray emitter mounted on the dorsal fin of the craft.

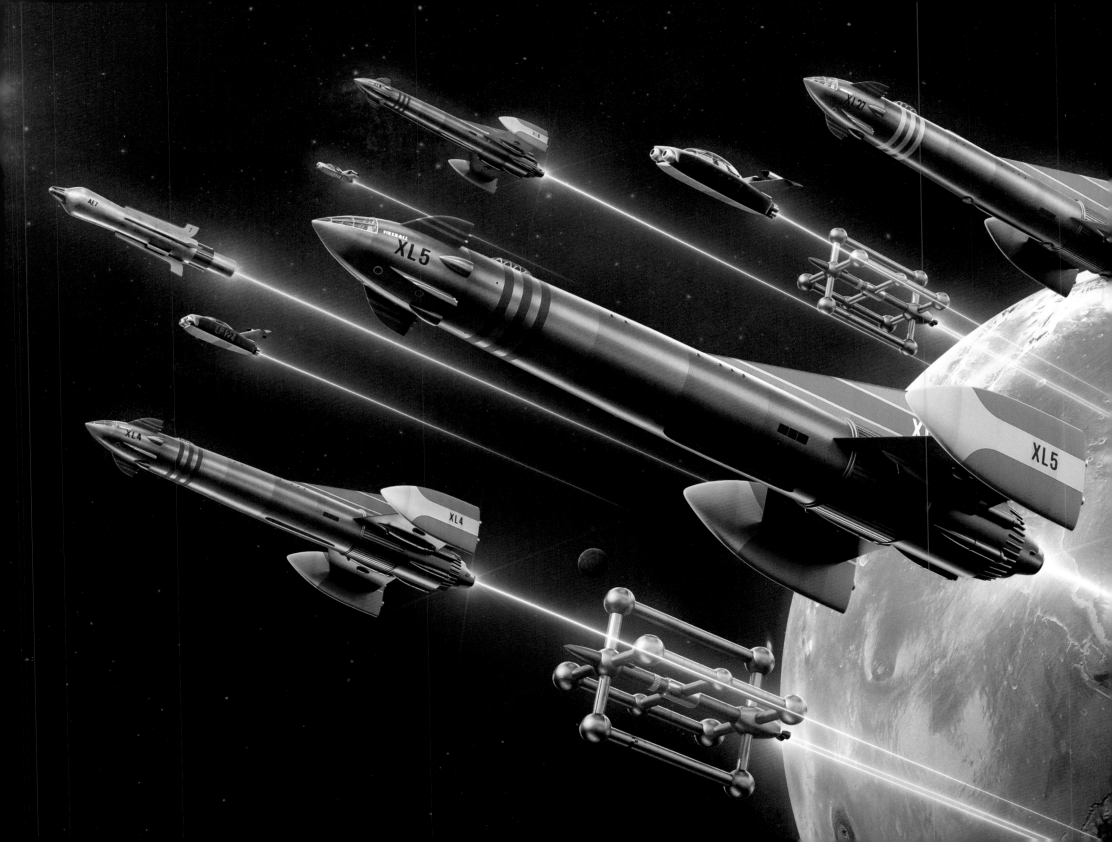

CLOSING REMARKS
from Commander Zero

We live in what many people consider a golden age of exploration and prosperity for humankind. Where once we were limited to a single planetary body, humanity now stands with the friends we have made in outer space as guardians of universal peace.

This peace, however, is fragile. Over the last few years, we have battled against rogue planets, terrible plagues and unstoppable machines. Earth nearly fell to hostile aliens that can manipulate the weather, a swarm of giant ants and an out-of-control cloud that burns everything it touches. Despite how far we have come as a species, the constant threat of losing it all through ignorance or complacency remains.

Over the course of this manual you have read about the history of our organisation, what we do and the hostile forces we face. Our aim was not just to give a transparent overview of the WSP but a sample of the life you would lead should you join our ranks.

It will not be easy. Each of us is held to the highest standard and once trained you will be on the fringes of the harshest frontier our kind has ever faced. As an astronaut of Earth, you will be expected to give your all – and if lives are on the line, possibly everything.

So knowing all this, everything you have read and factoring in the unknown, ask yourself, are you up to the challenge?

If the answer is yes then you are the person the WSP is looking for. Welcome aboard.

Commander Jonathan Wilbur Zero

FIREBALL XL5

Written by
CHRIS THOMPSON
ANDREW CLEMENTS

Illustrated by
CHRIS THOMPSON

Additional Illustrations by
CHRISTINA LOGAN

Edited by
STEPHANIE BRIGGS

Design by
AMAZING15

Produced by
JAMIE ANDERSON

Fireball XL5 created by
GERRY AND SYLVIA ANDERSON

WITH THANKS TO:
Tim Collins, David Hirsch

Fireball XL5 ™ and © ITC Entertainment Group 1963 and 2024.
Licensed by ITV Studios Limited. All Rights Reserved.

First published in the UK in 2024 by Anderson Entertainment

Hardback 978-1-914522-32-1

Printed at Interak Printing House, Poland

itv STUDIOS
GLOBAL ENTERTAINMENT

ANDERSON ENTERTAINMENT

GERRYANDERSON.COM